KU-022-128

Brain-Boosting Sequence Puzzles

Series Editor: Sarah Wells

Puzzle Contributors: Philip Carter,
Bernard Murray, Fran Pickering

Additional Contributors: Ann Marangos,
Peter Sorenti, Lucy Dear, Keely Borthwick

Page Design and Layout: Linley Clode

Cover Design: Alan Shiner

Published by:
LAGOON BOOKS
PO BOX 311, KT2 5QW, UK
PO BOX 990676, Boston, MA 02199, USA

www.lagoongames.com

ISBN: 1902813537

Printed in Singapore

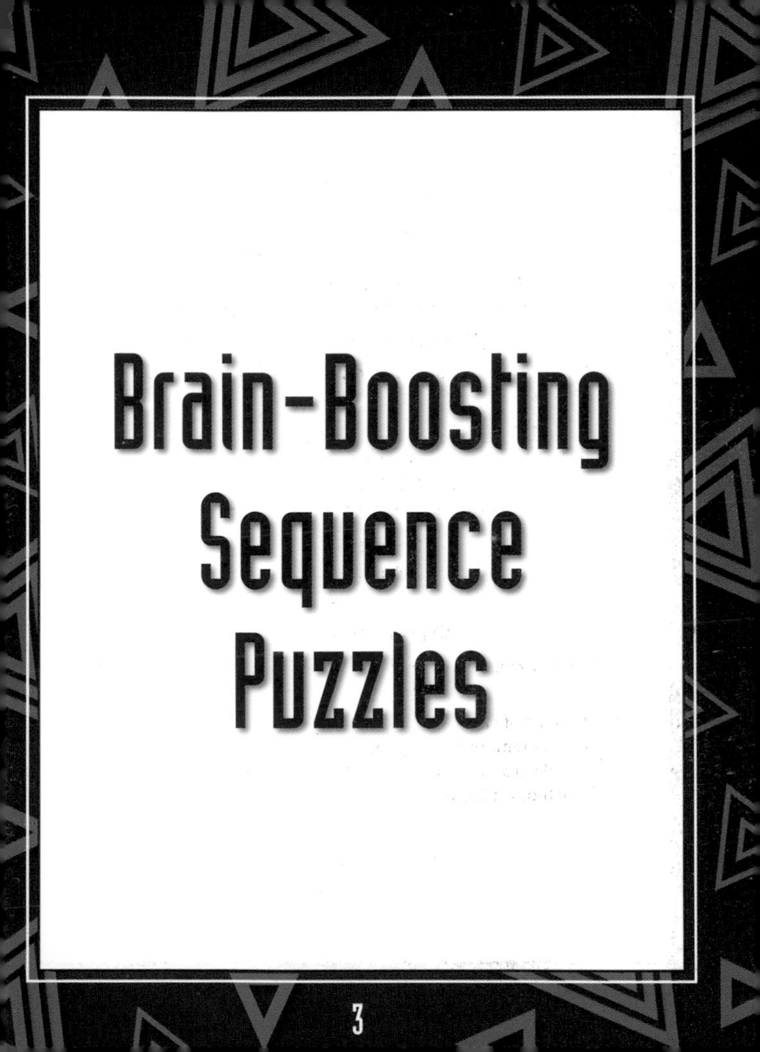

Brain-Boosting Sequence Puzzles

Introduction

In the same way that physical exercise tones your muscles and makes you fitter, doing puzzles exercises your IQ and hones your intellect.

It is on this basis that we have created this compilation of fun and challenging puzzles, to give you the ultimate cerebral workout.

Beautifully designed and cleverly illustrated, we have assembled nearly 100 of the best sequence puzzles, to challenge and enhance your powers of extrapolation.

Divided into four chapters, each puzzle has a score of 1, 2 or 3 points.

In **Chapter 1** – you will find the easiest puzzles, ones you should really be able to complete within 60 seconds.

In **Chapter 2** – you will find a slightly more difficult set of puzzles – ones that should be completed within 3 minutes.

In **Chapter 3** – there is a much more difficult range of conundrums, which should take about 5 minutes to crack.

And in **Chapter 4** – you will find the most fiendish puzzles that could take you up to 10 minutes to work out.

If you manage to solve the puzzles within the time limit allocated in each chapter, you can award yourself the points.

A helpful scoring card has been given at the beginning of each chapter to help you to keep score. When you have completed all the chapters, turn to see your overall score on page 191.

For those of you who want to test the theory that practice makes perfect, why not jump to the last chapter of the book and see how you fare?
If you solve the puzzle within 10 minutes, congratulations! You really are a puzzle genius.
If you do not, however, then go back to the beginning of the book and work through the puzzles in chronological order. By the time you reach Chapter 4, you should have no excuses – your score should have leapt up after all the practice.

If, by the end of the book, you have still not achieved your ultimate goal, and you want more practice, then turn to page 192 to see Lagoon's other Brain-Boosting titles.

Contents

	Page
Introduction	4&5
Chapter 1	7
Chapter 1 – Scoring	8
Chapter 2	53
Chapter 2 – Scoring	54
Chapter 3	99
Chapter 3 – Scoring	100
Chapter 4	145
Chapter 4 – Scoring	146
Overall Rating	191
Other Titles by Lagoon Books	192

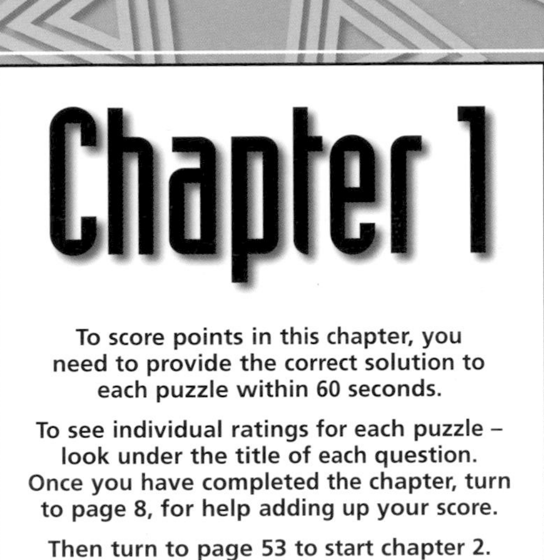

Chapter 1

To score points in this chapter, you need to provide the correct solution to each puzzle within 60 seconds.

To see individual ratings for each puzzle – look under the title of each question. Once you have completed the chapter, turn to page 8, for help adding up your score.

Then turn to page 53 to start chapter 2.

Chapter 1 - Scoring

Puzzle points for correct answer

Fruit Machine 1

Time Flies. 1

Different Darts 1

Feline Fun 3

Band Aid 1

Elevator 2

Color Me Puzzled! 1

Window Wonder. 3

Diary Dilemma 1

Whatever Next? 2

Roll the Dice 1

Face Facts 3

Play School 1

Extra Terrestrial. 2

Pool Cue 3

Flag Feat 1

Building Blocks 3

Classroom Conundrum . . 2

Olympic Parade 1

Number Crunching 2

Shifty Sequence. 2

Blocks of Color 3

YOUR TOTAL

40

Fruit Machine

Rating 1 Point

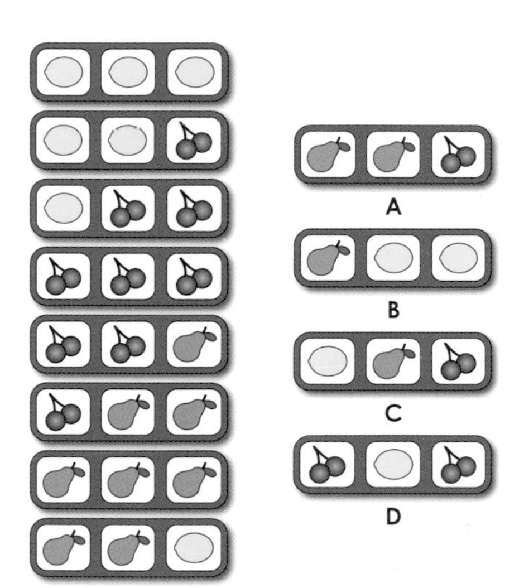

Which arcade machine display completes the sequence?

Fruit Machine - Solution

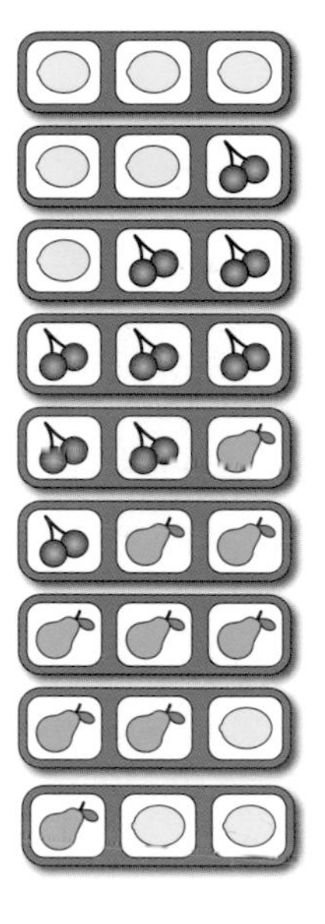

B.

Time Flies

Rating 1 Points

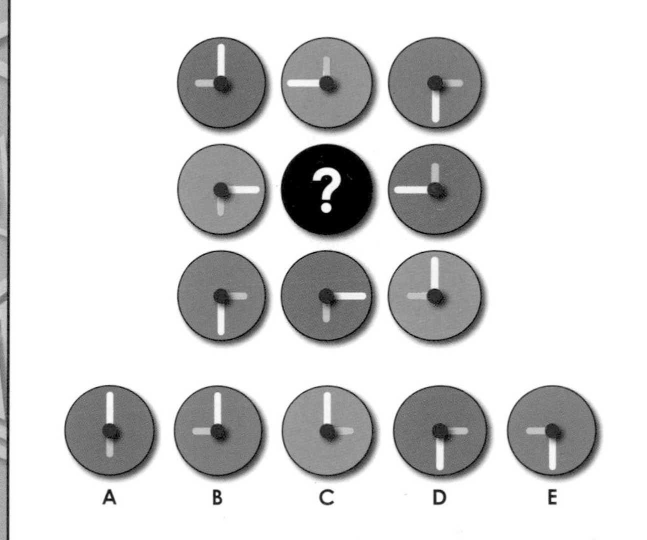

All the clocks in Mr Tock's clock shop have gone haywire. He notices that the clock faces seem to follow a sequence. One of the clocks is very dusty, so he can't see what time it's telling. Can you work out what time it says?

Time Flies - Solution

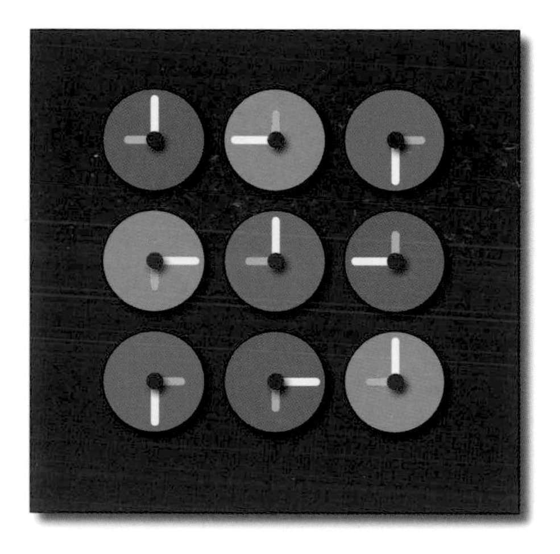

B.

Looking across the rows of clocks, the big hand moves 90° anti-clockwise and the small hand moves 90° clockwise. Looking down the columns of clocks, the big hand moves 90° clockwise and the small hand 90° anti-clockwise.

Different Darts

Rating 1 Point

Which number completes the sequence on this rather odd dartboard?

Different Darts – Solution

5 (or 625).
The larger numbers in each diagonally opposite pair of segments are multiples of the smaller number.

Feline Fun

Rating 3 Points

Which circus lion is the odd one out?

Feline Fun - Solution

Casper.
His name has 6 letters, all the others have 5.

Band Aid

Rating 1 Point

A B C D

A rock band is touring America. Their first four concerts are at Baltimore, Detroit, Fort Worth and Houston. Where will they perform next?

Band Aid - Solution

Jacksonville.
The initial letters of the venues are B, D, F, H, skipping a letter of the alphabet each time. Therefore the next venue should begin with 'J'

Elevator

Rating 2 Points

Sally decided to take the elevator from the second to the top floor. When she pushed the button the elevator was already on the 6th floor, after which it went up to the 8th floor, down to the 5th, back up to the 10th and down to the 3rd.

Sally decided to wait for the elevator because she knew that it would go up to the 11th floor, and then come down to the second. However, she knew that the elevator would then take her up to a certain floor whether she liked it or not.

How did she know, and which floor did it take her to?

Elevator - Solution

The elevator was operating in the sequence:
6, 8, 5, 10, 3, 11, 2, 13

There were two alternate sequences, up and down.
The down sequence progressed – 1, – 2, – 1, etc
and the up sequence progressed + 2, + 1, + 2 etc.

The next floor the elevator would visit is 13.

Color Me Puzzled!

Rating 1 Point

Betty bought a new coloring book. One page showed an outdoor scene with the above sequence printed on it, instead of a title. Can you complete the sequence and work out the title of the page?

Color Me Puzzled! - Solution

R2 O5 Y5 G4 B3 I5 V5

RAINBOW

The next in the sequence is V5.
The title of the page is 'RAINBOW'. The sequence shows the first letter of the name of each color, in order, plus the number of letters remaining in the name.

Window Wonder

Rating 3 Points

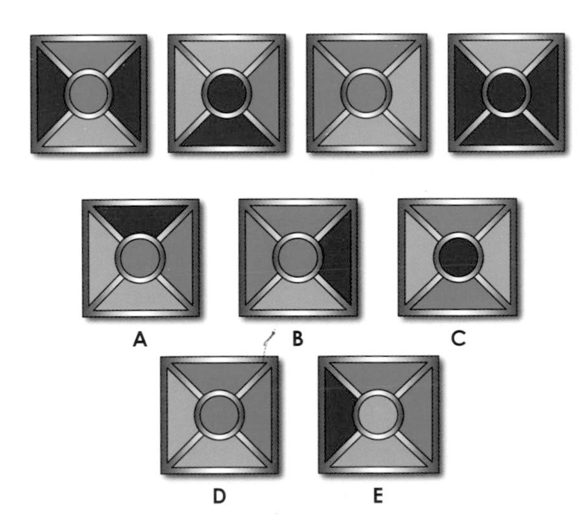

The Institute of Mathematics is planning to put 5 stained glass windows into a wall. The first 4 windows are shown above. Which window will complete the sequence?

Window Wonder - Solution

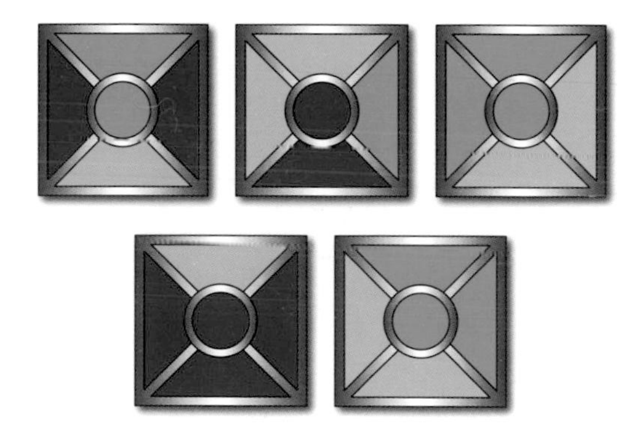

D.

The middle circle alternates blue/red, the north segment alternates blue/green, the east segment alternates red/blue/green, the south segment alternates green/red and the west segment alternates red/green/blue.

Diary Dilemma

Rating 1 Point

Flicking through his diary, Ben noticed the sequence shown above. What is the next letter in the sequence?

Diary Dilemma - Solution

F.
They are the initial letters of the months of the year, in reverse order.

Whatever Next?

Rating 2 Points

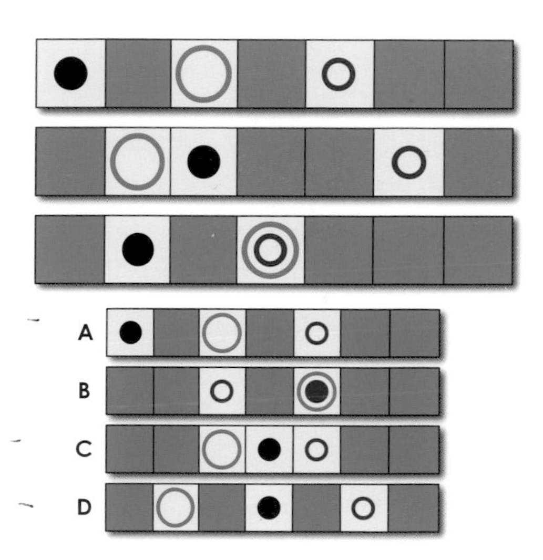

From the sequence above, can you work out what comes next?

Whatever Next? - Solution

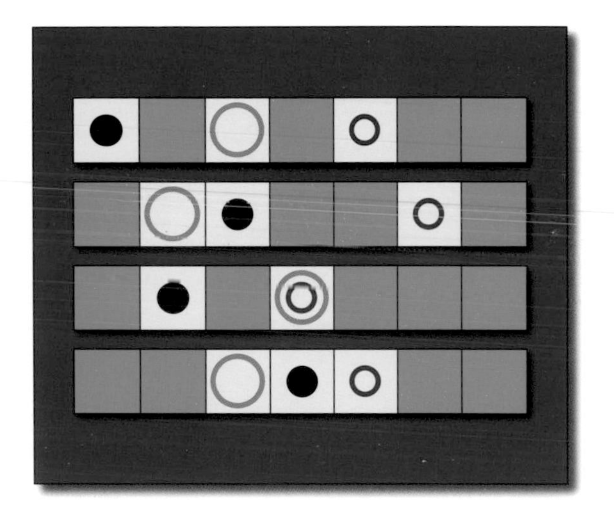

C.

Each figure moves in the following sequence:
The black dot moves two forward , one back;
the red circle moves one forward, two back and
the circle moves one back two forward.

Roll the Dice

Rating 1 Point

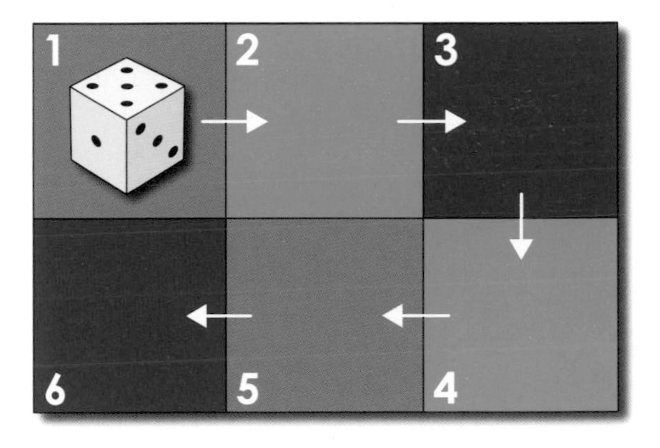

A dice is rolled one face at a time from square 1 to square 2 etc, in the direction of the arrows and finishing in square 6. What number will be face upwards on the dice when it arrives in square 6?

Roll the Dice - Solution

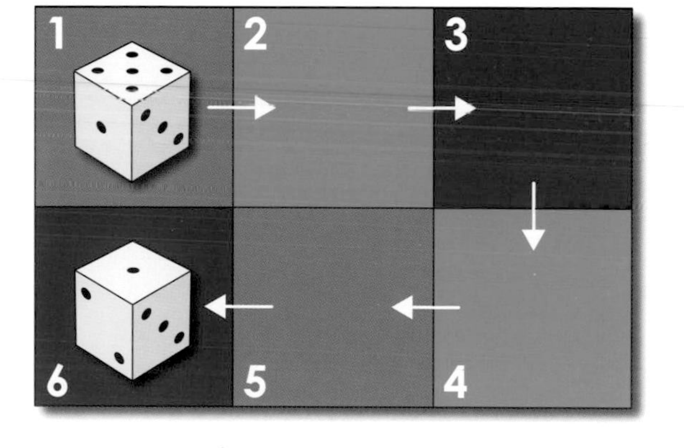

1.

Face Facts

Rating 3 Points

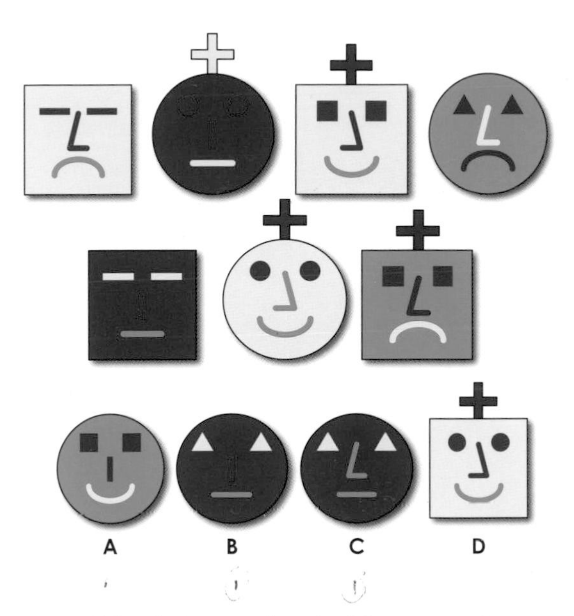

What is the next face in this sequence?

Face Facts - Solution

B.

The two face shapes rotate, the 3 types of noses rotate, the 4 shapes of eyes rotate, and the cross appears on the head when the eye shape is the same as the head shape.

Play School

Rating 1 Point

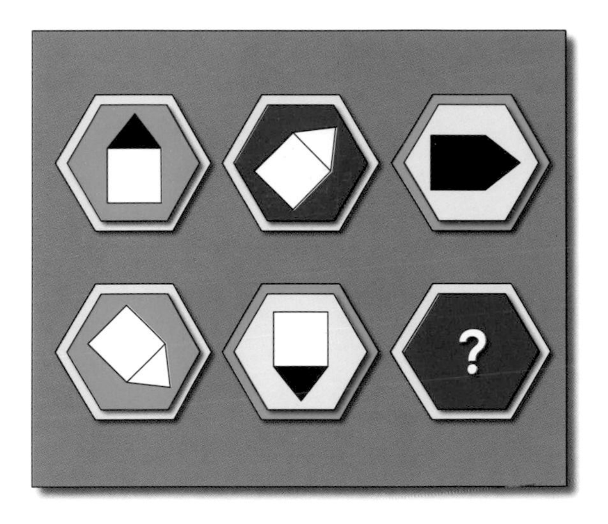

Alfie was playing with some shapes at nursery.
Being a clever child he worked out
what the next logical shape was. Can you?

Play School - Solution

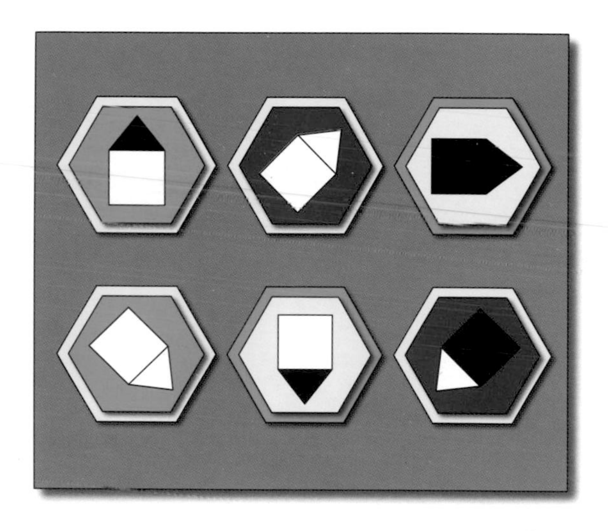

The whole figure rotates 45 degrees clockwise each time, the triangle proceeds black, white, black, white, while the square proceeds white, white black, white, white, black etc.

Extra Terrestrial

Rating 2 Points

Three symbols were sent to an alien spaceship to assess their powers of logic. What would be the next symbol if the ETs understood the sequence correctly?

Extra Terrestrial - Solution

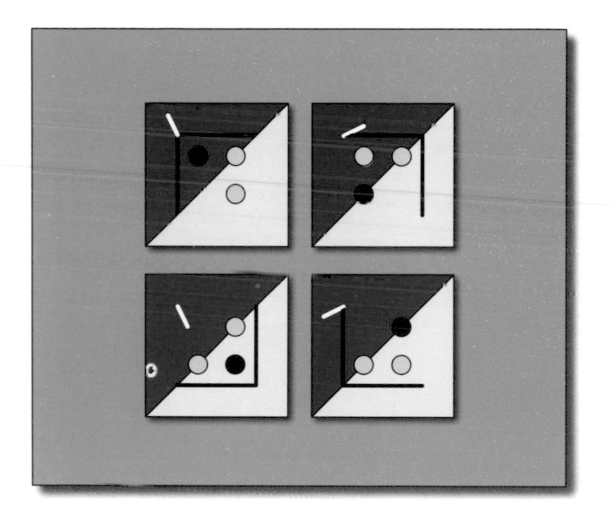

The right angle turns 90 degrees clockwise each time, the three balls revolve 90 degrees anti-clockwise, and the line at the top left turns 90 degrees clockwise.

Pool Cue

Rating 3 Points

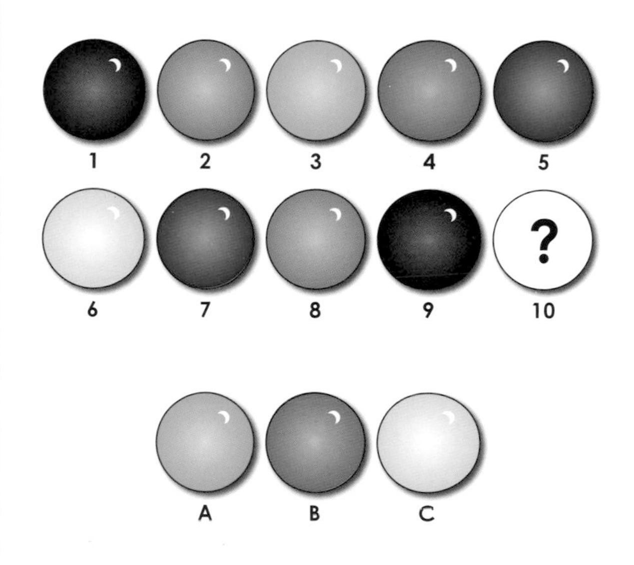

Paul has created a new version of pool, in which all of the colored balls have to be potted twice in a particular order. The first nine are potted in the order shown above. What is the next ball to be potted?

Pool Cue - Solution

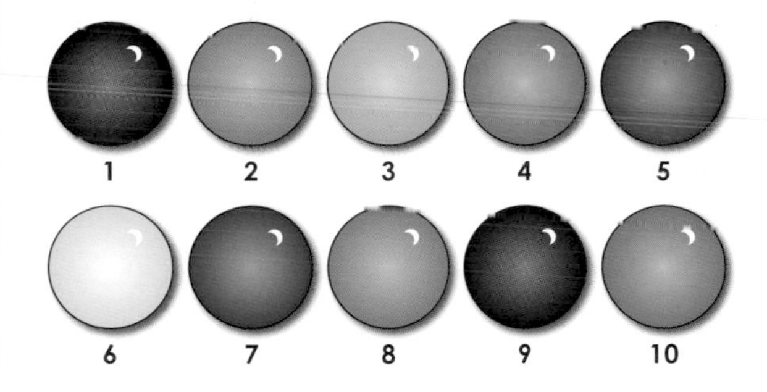

Pink.
The order is the six colours in alphabetical order from the beginning of each word, followed by alphabetical order of each word in reverse.

Flag Feat

Rating 1 Point

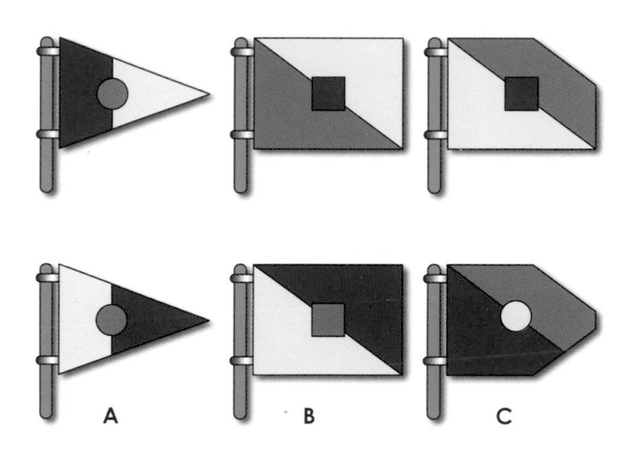

In this sequence of naval flags, what would be the fourth one to be raised?

Flag Feat - Solution

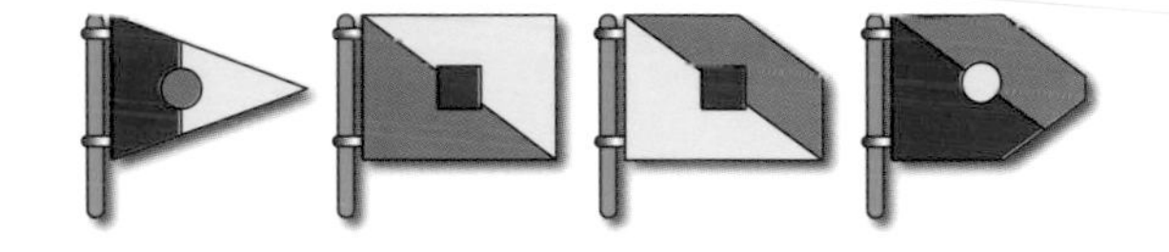

C.
The number of sides of each flag
increases by one each time.

Building Blocks

Rating 3 Points

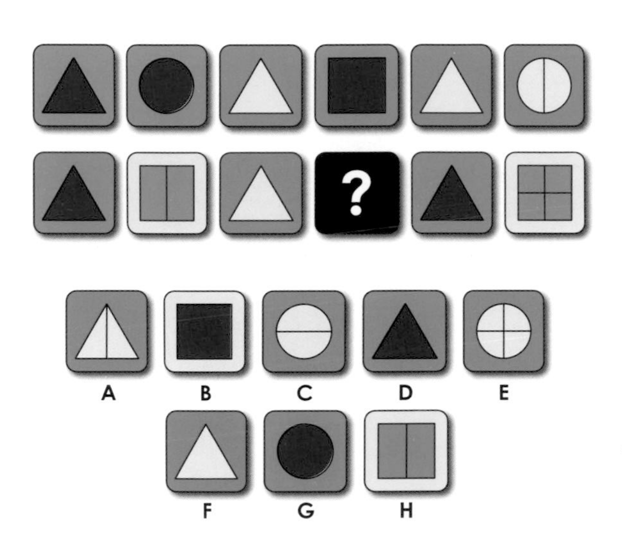

Oscar is two years old, and is already showing signs of becoming a mathematical genius. He's playing with his bricks, and has laid them out in the pattern shown. He's trying to find the missing brick in the sequence. Can you help him?

Building Blocks - Solution

E.

Every alternate figure is a triangle. Between them is the sequence circle/square. Each time the circle and square appear a line is added first vertically, then horizontally. The figures colored red have an additional figure between them at each stage.

Classroom Conundrum

Rating 2 Points

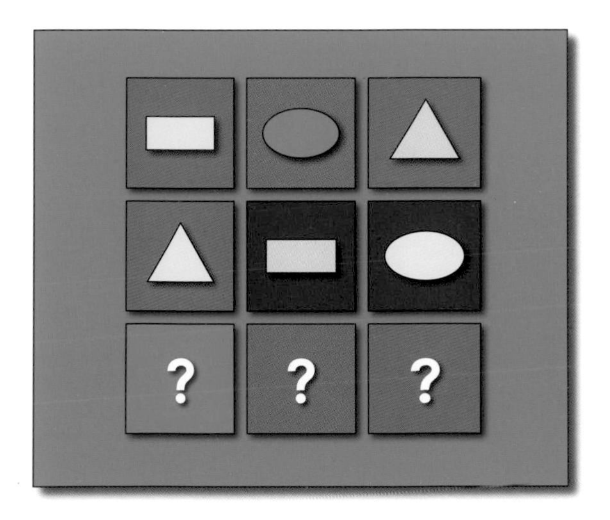

Professor Pringle liked to keep his students on their toes. Every so often he would draw a puzzle on the blackboard for them to solve. Here's one of them. Can you complete the sequence?

Classroom Conundrum - Solution

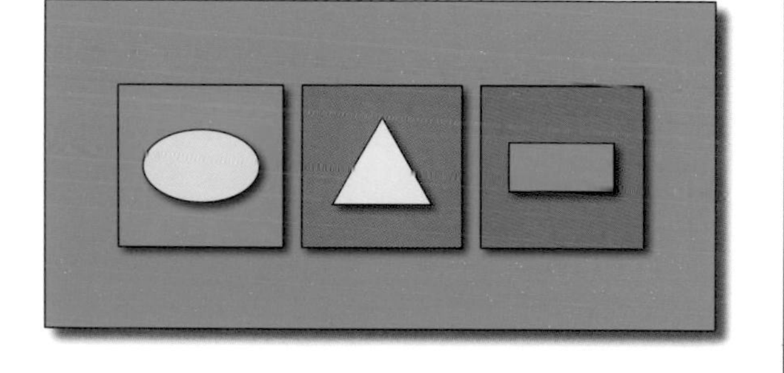

Shapes move one place along to the right.

Olympic Parade

Rating 1 Point

Scotland	Estonia	Quatar	Uruguay
Ethiopia	Norway	China	?

A. Zimbabwe B. Austria C. Iraq D.Egypt E. Spain

At the opening ceremony of the Olympics, the countries began the parade in the order shown above. Can you work out which country came next in the sequence?

Olympic Parade - Solution

Scotland	**E**stonia	**Q**uatar	**U**ruguay
Ethiopia	**N**orway	**C**hina	**E**gypt

SEQUENCE

Egypt.
The initial letters of the countries spell out the word 'SEQUENCE'.

Number Crunching

Rating 2 Points

"Can you tell me the missing number in this sequence – 3, ?, 4, 2, 3, 7, 6, 2, 4, 8?"

"So what's the missing number here – 2, 5, 3, ?, 6, 4?"

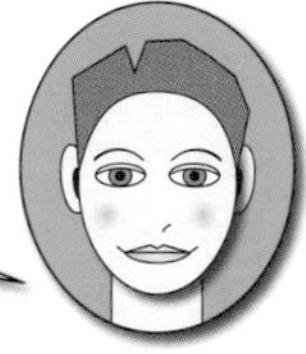

"So what number comes between four and four in this sequence – 2, 4, 6, 5, 7, 4, ?, 4, 2, 4, 9?"

From the illustration, the answer to the first question is 3.The answer to the second question is 7. Can you work out the answer to the third question?

Number Crunching - Solution

"Can you tell me
the missing number in
this sequence –
3, 3, 4, 2, 3, 7, 6, 2, 4, 8?"

"So what's the missing
number here –
2, 5, 3, 3, 6, 4?"

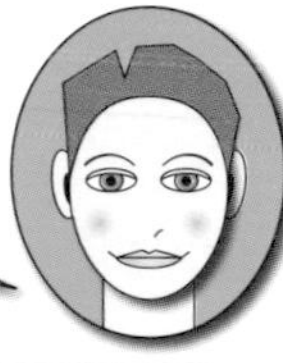

"So what number comes
between four and four
in this sequence –
2, 4, 6, 5, 7, 4, 3, 4, 2, 4, 9?"

3.
Each number represents the number of
letters in each word of the question.

Shifty Sequence

Rating 2 Points

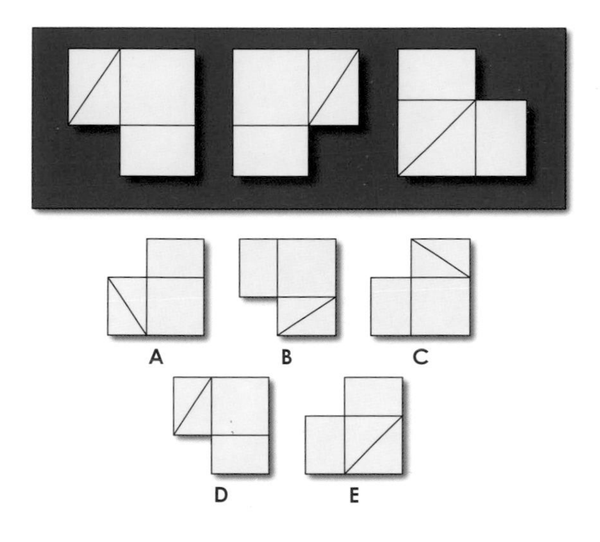

From the sequence above, can you work out what comes next?

Shifty Sequence - Solution

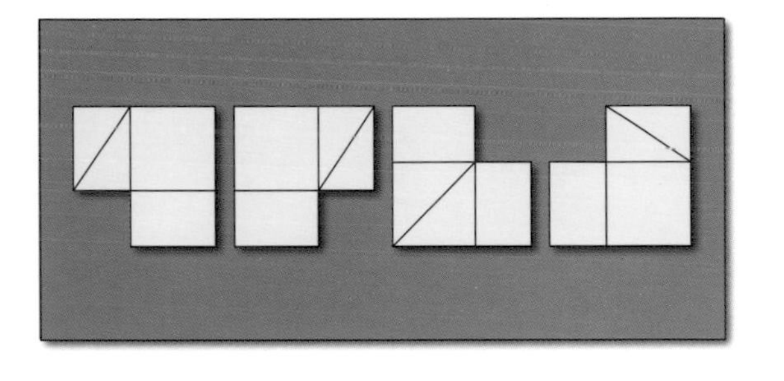

C.

At each stage the figure rotates 90° anti-clockwise and the line is in a different segment, also working anti-clockwise

Blocks of Color

Rating 3 Points

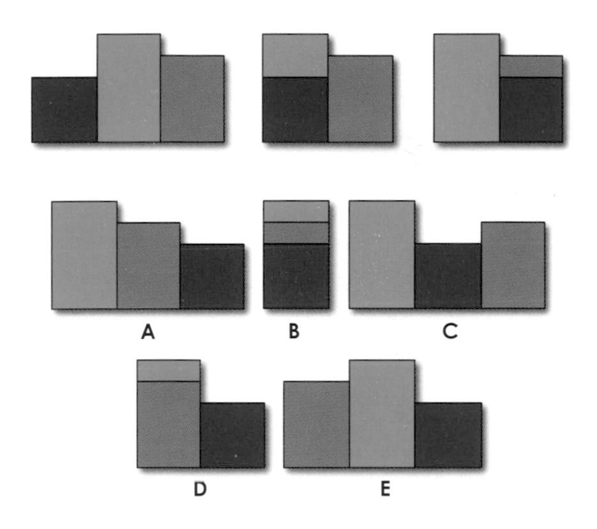

These images follow a sequence.
Can you see which comes next?

Blocks of Color - Solution

A.
The red square moves from left
to right one place at a time.

Chapter 2

To score points in this chapter, you need to provide the correct solution to each puzzle within three minutes.

To see individual ratings for each puzzle – look under the title of each question. Once you have completed the chapter, turn to page 54, for help adding up your score.

Then turn to page 99 to start chapter 3.

Chapter 2 - Scoring

Puzzle points for correct answer

Puzzle	Points	Puzzle	Points
Pendant Problem	**1**	Cave Drawing	**3**
Steeplechase	**2**	Number Link	**2**
Serial Cereal	**1**	Song Sequence	**1**
Reign of Glory	**3**	Problematic Promise	**1**
Seating Plan	**1**	Drive You Dotty	**2**
Meter Malfunction	**2**	It's a Lottery	**3**
Aztec	**3**	Rainbow	**1**
Clock Calamity	**1**	Chalky Challenge	**2**
Puzzle Fiend	**1**	Ever Increasing Circles	**3**
Control Panel	**2**	Niggling Numbers	**1**
ET Message	**2**	Figure Fiddle	**2**

YOUR TOTAL

/ **40**

Pendant Problem

Rating 1 Point

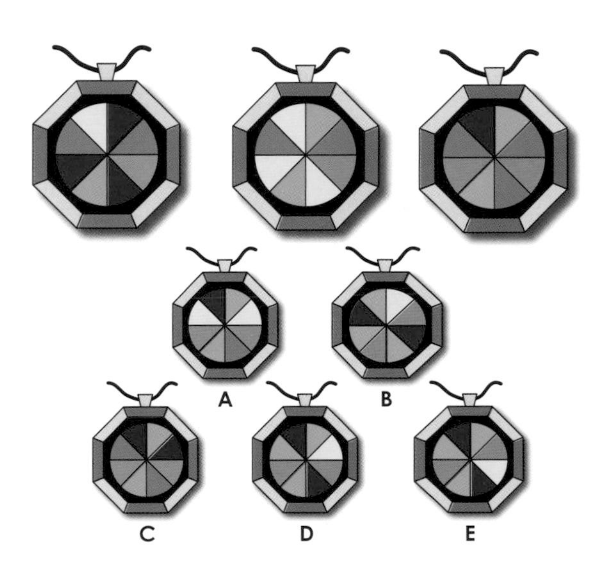

Each year for the past three years the Pharaoh has given his wife a pendant on her birthday. The patterns on the pendants follow a pattern. Can you work out what pendant he will give her next year?

Pendant Problem - Solution

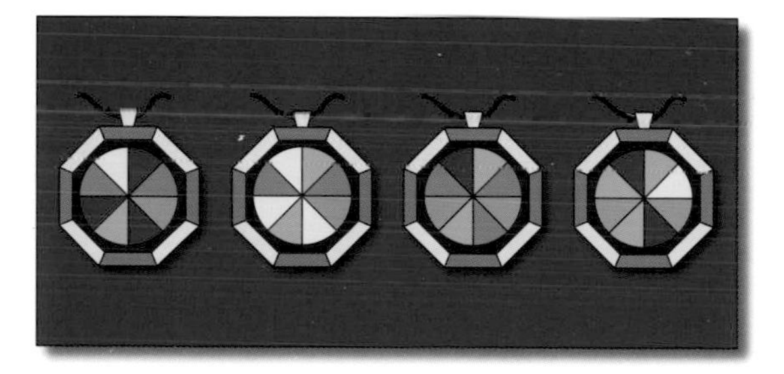

D.
At each stage the three segments which are the same color are discarded and three new colored segments replace them.

Steeplechase

Rating 2 Points

Horse number 3 won the race by a short head followed by horse number 20. What was the number of the horse who came last?

Steeplechase - Solution

6.
Read the numbers backwards from first to last to reveal the sequence 30, 29, 28, 27, 26 (62, 72, 82, 92, 03)

Serial Cereal

Rating 1 Point

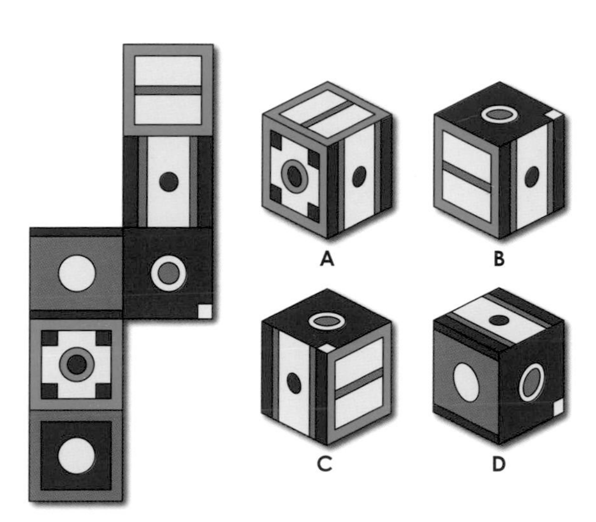

One rainy day, Jane made her small son some stacking bricks from empty cereal packets. Before she stuck the last one together, she tried to guess which of the others it would look like. Which one will it look like when finished?

Serial Cereal – Solution

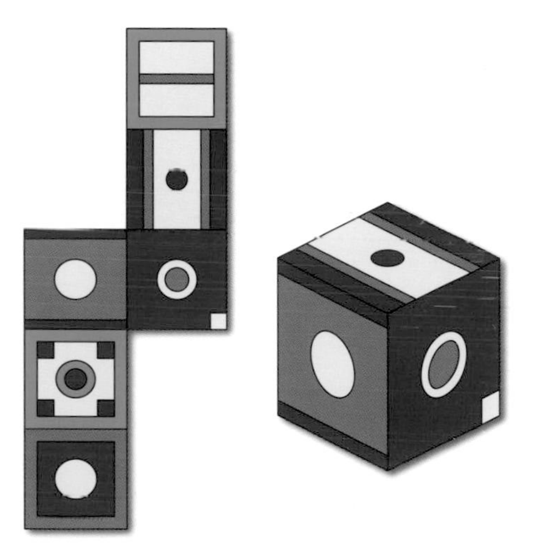

It will look like D.

Reign of Glory

Rating 3 Points

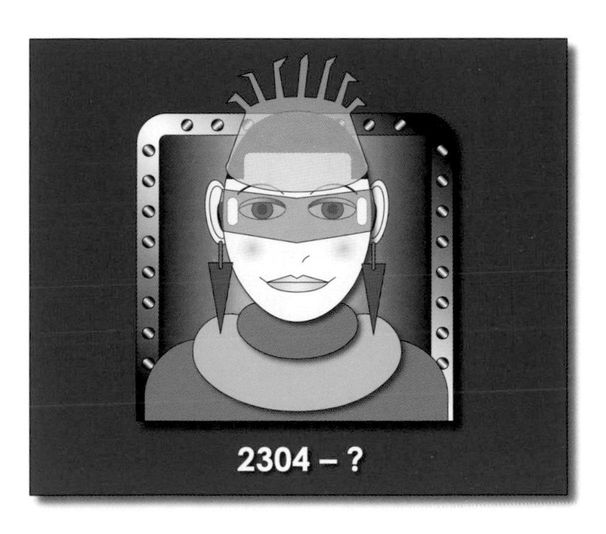

In the twenty-third century, there was a move away from republics back to monarchies. King Bob reigned from 2211 to 2230, King Dave from 2230 to 2262 and King Tim from 2262 to 2304. If King Ken ascended the throne in 2304, when did his reign end?

Reign of Glory - Solution

2334.
Each letter of every king's name is converted to its numerical equivalent and added together – A = 1, B = 2 etc. Therefore Ken = 30.

Seating Plan

Rating 1 Point

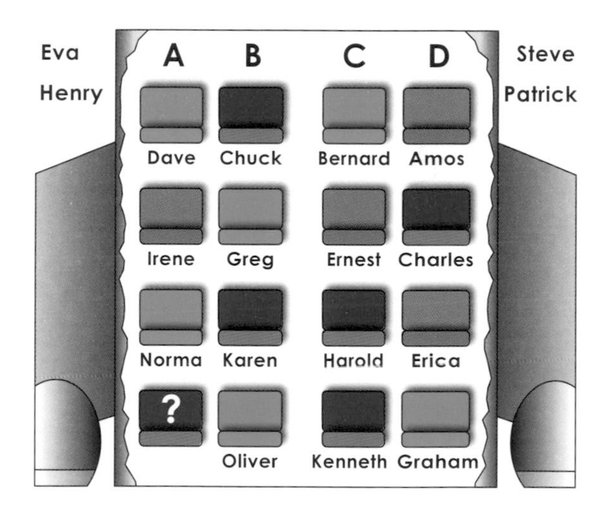

In the aircraft seating plan shown, who should occupy the empty seat – Eva, Henry, Steve or Patrick?

Seating Plan - Solution

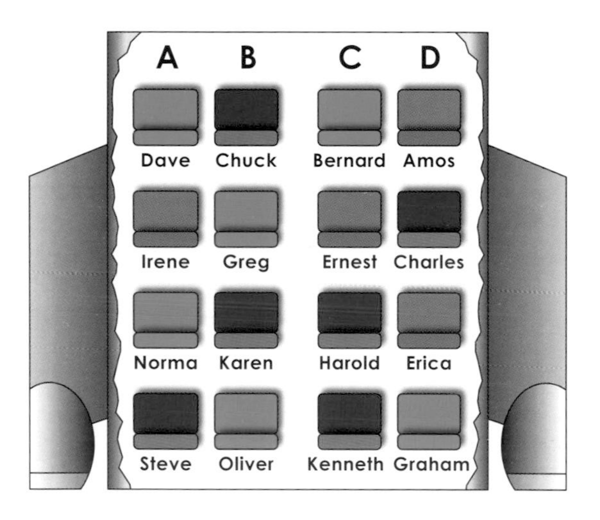

Steve.
The initial letters of column D skip 2 places each time A, C, E G. Column C skips 3 places, column B skips 4 places, and column A skips 5 places.

Meter Malfunction

Rating 2 Points

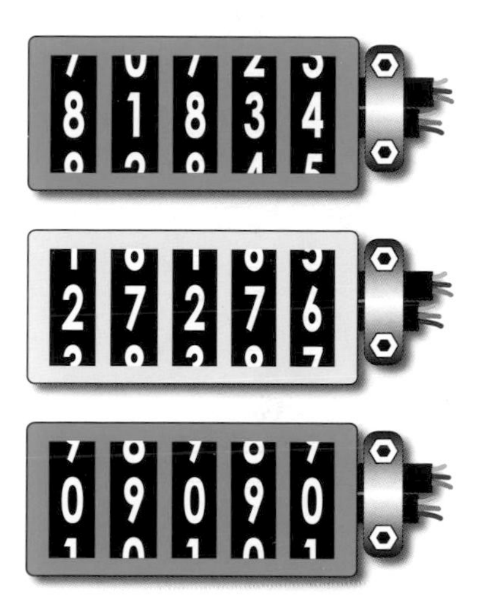

There is something wrong with Joanna's electricity meter. On checking it each day, she records the readings shown. What will tomorrow's reading be?

Meter Malfunction - Solution

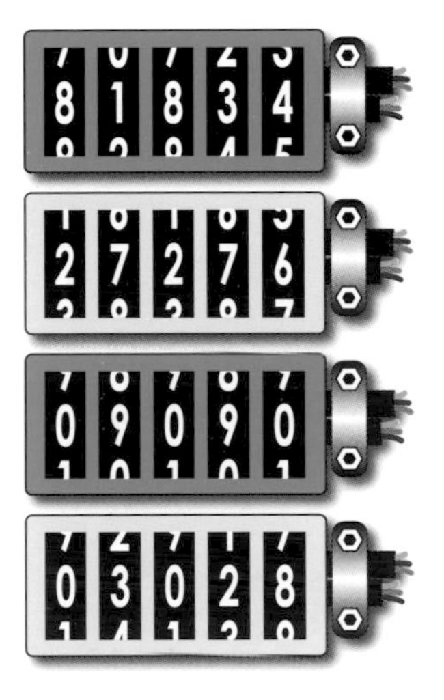

Divide the previous reading by three,
then deduct 2 from the last digit.

Aztec

Rating 3 Points

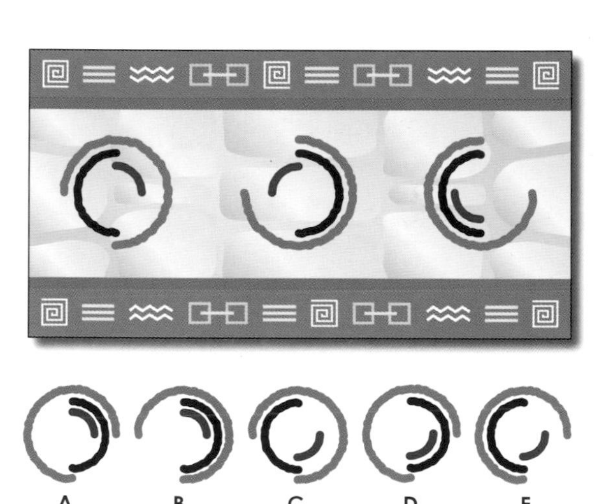

Cincinnati Scott has entered the ancient city of Paxolotl. On a wall he spots a series of illustrations. He believes that they're some kind of puzzle, but he isn't having much luck finding a solution. Can you help him?

Aztec - Solution

D.

The outer arc moves 90° clockwise at each stage, the middle arc moves 180° at each stage, and the inner arc moves 90° anti-clockwise at each stage.

Clock Calamity

Rating 1 Point

Brian's digital clock is malfunctioning.
Its timekeeping is consistent, but follows a logic of its own. Can you complete the sequence?

Clock Calamity - Solution

06.40.
The clock gains an extra 2 hours and 5 minutes each hour, so the next step would be 8 hours and 20 minutes ahead of the previous time.

Puzzle Fiend

Rating 1 Point

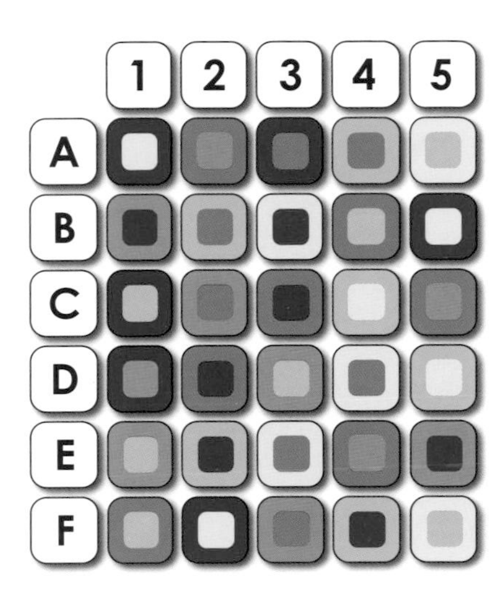

The puzzle-mad editor of 'Puzzles Galore' was also a security fanatic. Every evening before he went home, he locked the solutions to his new puzzles in a safe, which had a computerized puzzle for a lock. If the first two keys are F2 and E3, can you work out the correct sequence of buttons on this safe keypad to open the door?

Puzzle Fiend - Solution

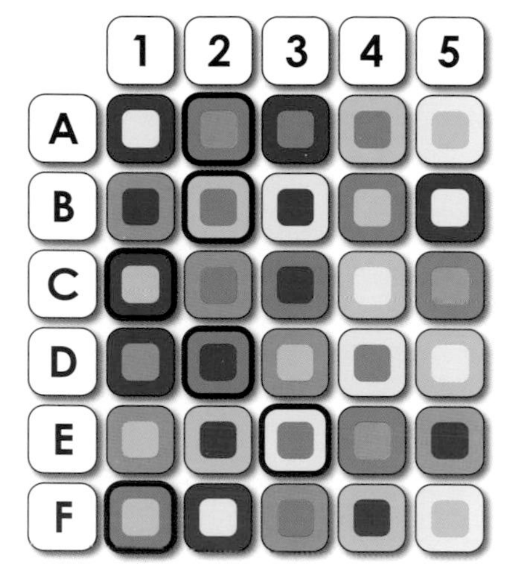

F2/ E3/ D2/ C1/ B2/ A2.
The middle color becomes the surrounding color in the next row up.

Control Panel

Rating 2 Points

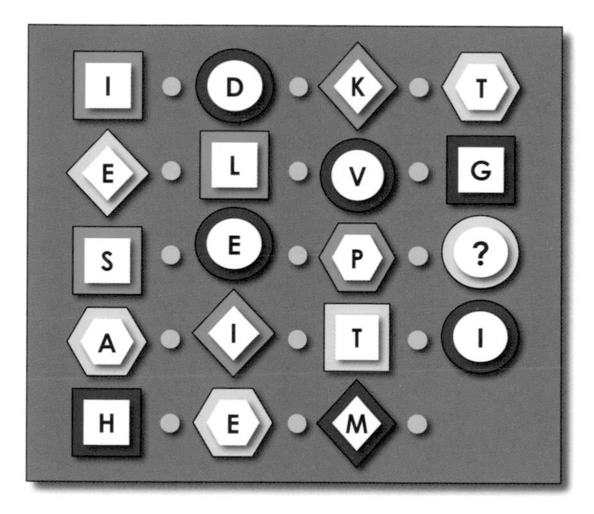

The Superstar Stadium had an audiovisual system with a central operating pad shown above. What letter should replace the question mark?

Control Panel - Solution

O.
The square buttons spell out LIGHTS.
The diamond buttons spell MIKE.
The hexagons spell TAPE.
The circles spell VIDEO.

ET Message

Rating 2 Points

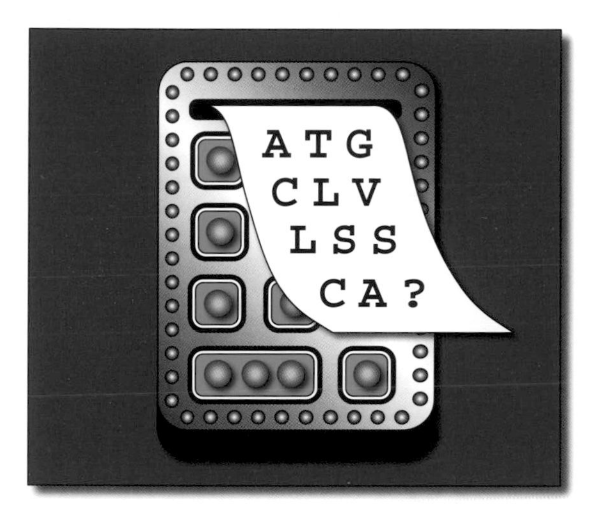

The Search for Extra-Terrestrial Intelligence Agency picked up a string of seemingly meaningless letters from one of their space probes. However, they noticed a sequence developing and worked out what the next letter should be – can you?

ET Message - Solution

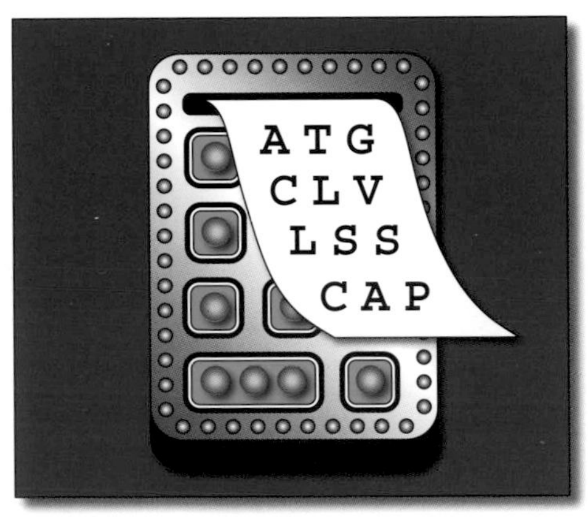

Pisces

P.

Each letter is the initial letter of an astrological sign in sequence through the year. The next one is P for Pisces.

Cave Drawing

Rating 3 Points

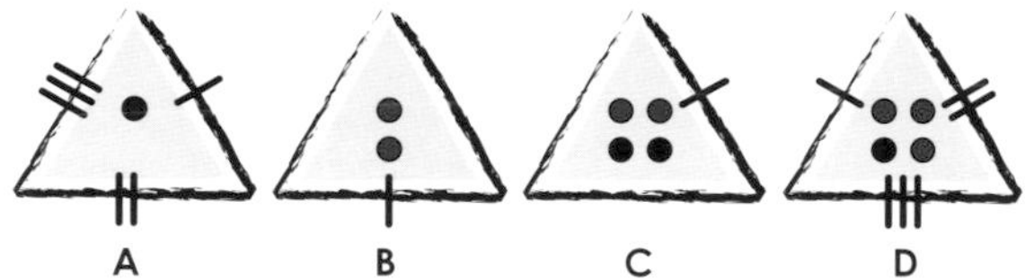

Grog the caveman is bored, so to pass the time he's drawing on the wall of his cave. After he's drawn three shapes, he notices a sequence. Can you work out what he should draw next to continue the sequence?

Cave Drawing - Solution

C.
Circles are added to the triangle one at a time, black and red alternately. Bisecting lies move clockwise, with the largest amount disappearing each time.

Number Link

Rating 2 Points

1 2 4 14

? 22 24

What is the missing number in this sequence?

Number Link - Solution

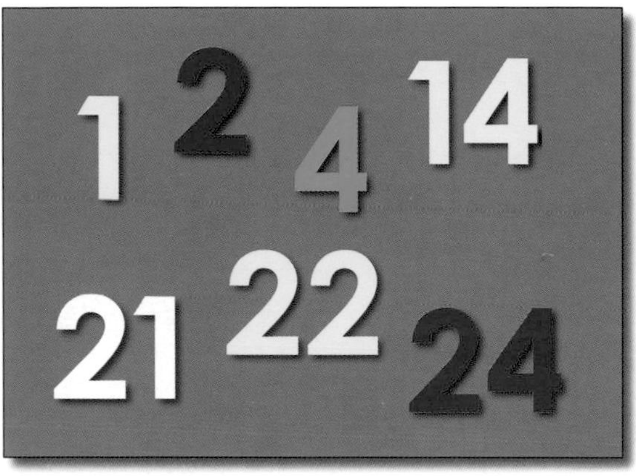

ONE, TWO, FOUR, FOURTEEN
TWENTY ONE, TWENTY TWO, TWENTY FOUR

21.
All are numbers which, when written, contain the letter 'O'.

Song Sequence

Rating 1 Point

"Why are there question marks at the bottom of the hymn board?" asked a new member of the congregation. *"That's the number of the sixth hymn"* explained one of the regular church-goers. *"Each week the Priest sets the final hymn number as a puzzle for the congregation"*. Can you work out what number the sixth hymn should be?

Song Sequence - Solution

212.
Reading downwards and changing boundaries, the sequence of odd numbers appears – 1, 3, 5, 7, 9, 11, 13, 15, 17, 19, 21, 23.

Problematic Promise

Rating 1 Point

Jon has developed a new gadget. It's a heptagonal dial showing different colored flashing circles. Every second the red circle moves three segments clockwise and the yellow circle moves four segments anti-clockwise. Jon has told his mother that he'll do his homework when the red circle and the yellow circle are in the same segment. In how many seconds will this be?

Problematic Promise – Solution

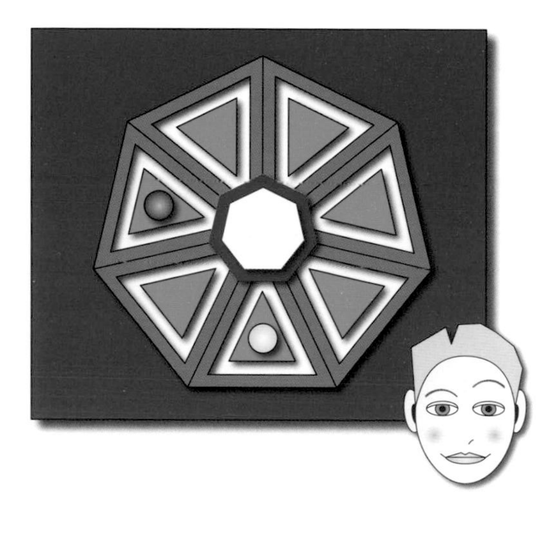

Never. In a heptagon three places clockwise is the same as four places anti-clockwise. They will always, therefore, remain the same distance apart.

Drive You Dotty

Rating 2 Points

If six of these dominoes were arranged in a triangle (with 2 each side), so that each side of the triangle had the same number of dots and no matching sides met, which one would be the odd one out?

Drive You Dotty - Solution

It's a Lottery!

Rating 3 Points

In this sequence of lottery balls, which ball is immediately to the right of the ball which is two to the left of the ball which is four to the right of the ball that is one more in value than the ball immediately to the right of the 4 ball?

It's a Lottery! - Solution

Rainbow

Rating 1 Point

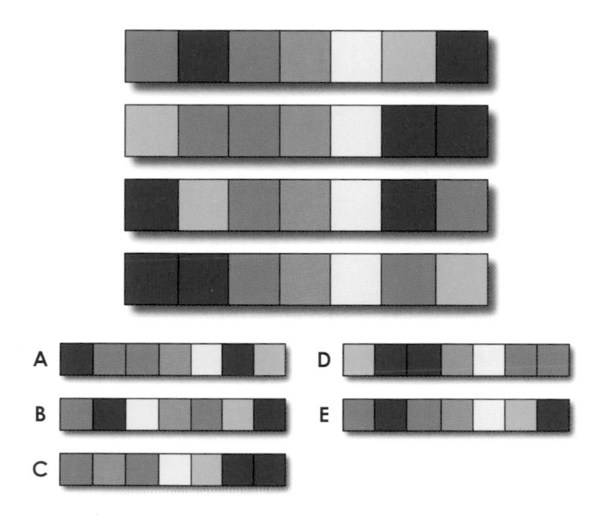

Can you work out what comes next in this sequence?

Rainbow - Solution

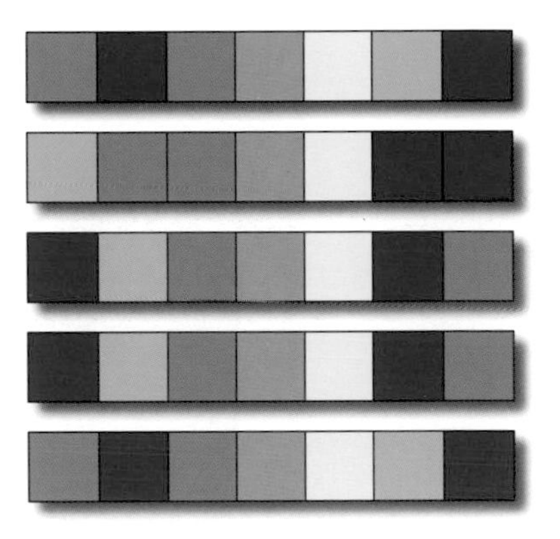

E.

At each stage the color next to the end on the left moves to the extreme right, and the color next to the end on the right moves to the extreme left.

Chalky Challenge

Rating 2 Point

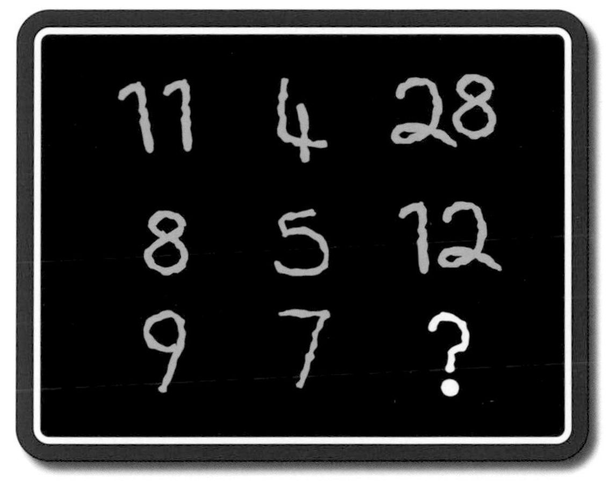

Which number completes
the sequence on the blackboard?

Chalky Challenge - Solution

11	4	28
8	5	12
9	7	8

8.
In each row, subtract the second number from the first then multiply by 4.

Ever Increasing Circles

Rating 3 Points

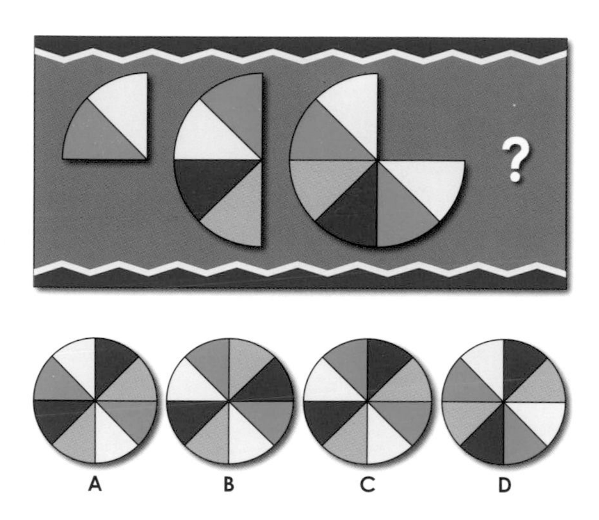

Lucy is designing a pattern for some fabric. She's drawn the beginnings of a pattern above, but is having problems working out what should come next. Can you help?

Ever Increasing Circles - Solution

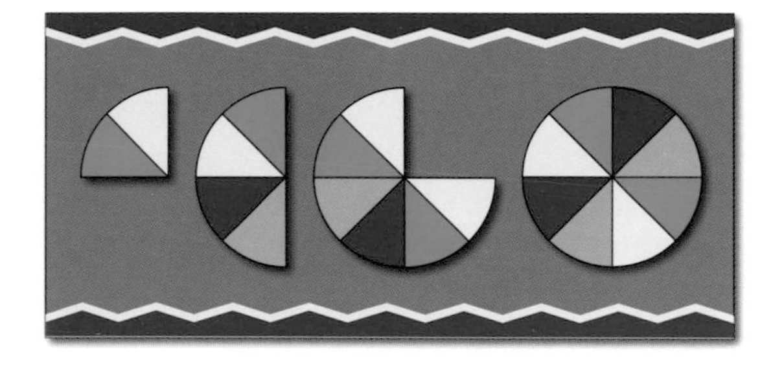

C.
At each stage another quarter is added. Opposite quarters contain the same colors, but not in opposite segments. At each stage the colors in each quarter swap round.

Niggling Numbers

Rating 1 Point

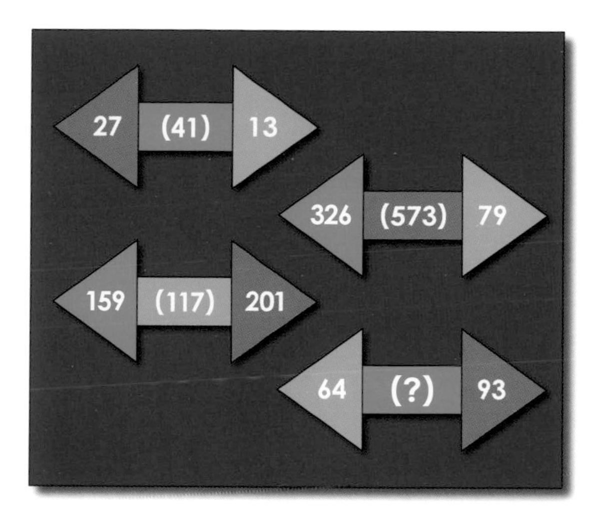

Can you fill in the number that completes the sequence?

Niggling Numbers - Solution

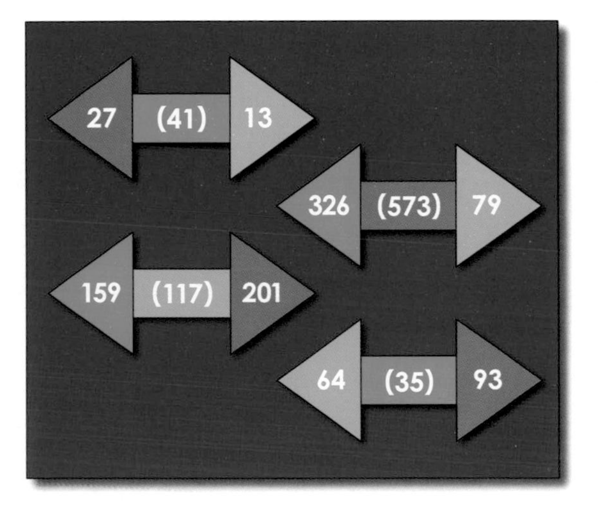

35.
The figure inside the brackets is the result of doubling the figure before the brackets and subtracting the one after them.

Figure Fiddle

Rating 2 Points

7396
5362

4068

This sum is correct, but none of the working out is shown. Can you see how to obtain the total shown?

Figure Fiddle - Solution

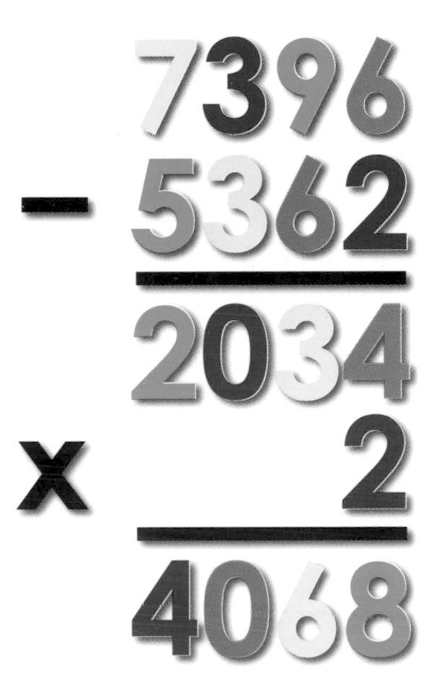

Subtract the middle line from the one above, then multiply the answer by 2.

To score points in this chapter, you need to provide the correct solution to each puzzle within five minutes.

To see individual ratings for each puzzle – look under the title of each question. Once you have completed the chapter, turn to page 100, for help adding up your score.

Then turn to page 145 to start chapter 4.

Chapter 3 - Scoring

Puzzle points for correct answer

Puzzle	Points	Puzzle	Points
Fruity Fun	**1**	Table Arrangement	**3**
Goalie!	**2**	DIY Disaster	**2**
Library Link	**1**	Round the World	**1**
Interior Design	**3**	Strange Sequence	**1**
Awful Architect	**1**	Math Muddle	**2**
Magic Square	**1**	Sweet Success	**3**
Big Cat Bother	**2**	Gridlock	**2**
Daylight Robbery	**2**	Accessorize	**1**
Shape Shift	**3**	Spy School	**2**
Geography Guess	**1**	Perplexing Pattern	**3**
Thirsty Work	**2**	Howzat!	**1**

YOUR TOTAL

/ **40**

Fruity Fun

Rating 1 Point

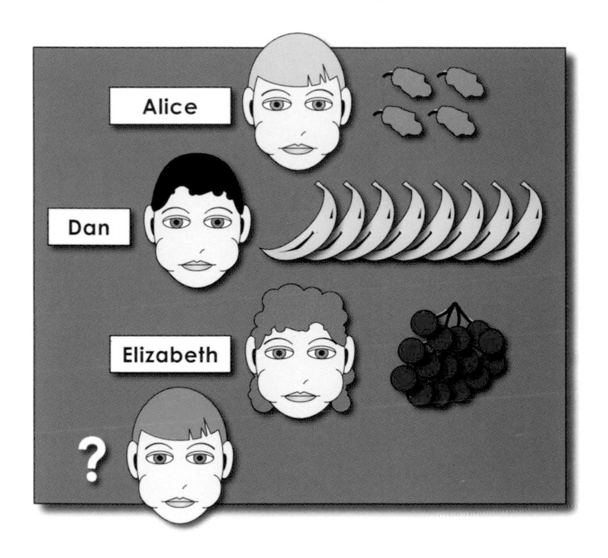

If Alice eats 4 dates, Don eats 8 bananas and Elizabeth eats 15 cherries, then how many figs does Florence eat?

Fruity Fun - Solution

36 figs.
Convert the initial letter of each person and the initial letter of each fruit to its numerical equivalent and multiply the two together for the number of fruit eaten.

Goalie!

Rating 2 Points

Newchester United used four different goalkeepers in four weeks, due to injuries. The fourth goalkeeper also became injured in the last match. Which of the following reserve goalkeepers will they use next Saturday?

Goalie! - Solution

C.
The six colors cycle from top to bottom.

Library Link

Rating 1 Point

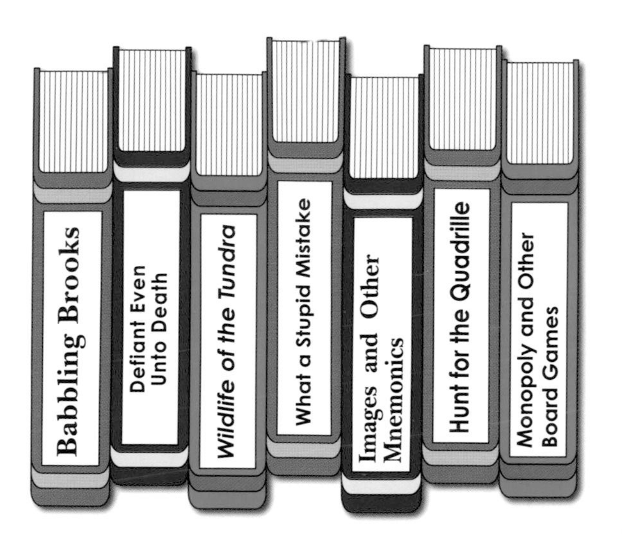

Mrs Biblio the librarian has made a list of books that need to be reordered. As she gives it a final check, she notices a pattern, and that one book title does not follow the pattern. Which book title does not follow the pattern?

Library Link - Solution

Hunt for the Quadrille.
Others have alternately 2 and 3 adjacent letters of the alphabet.

Interior Design

Rating 3 Points

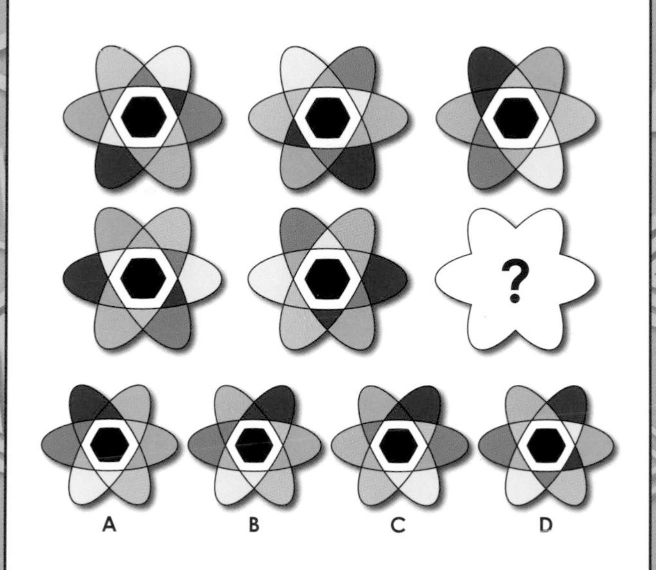

Joanna is painting a floral pattern on her bedroom wall.Which flower should she paint next?

Interior Design - Solution

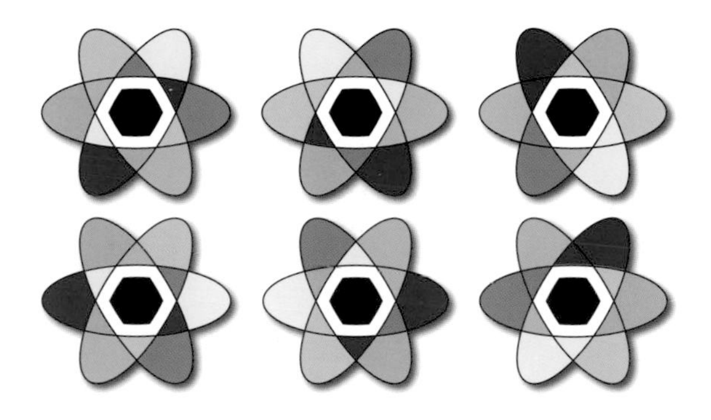

B.

Outer colors alternately move one place anti-clockwise, then swap places with their opposite color. Inner colors, swap places, then move one place clockwise, alternately.

Awful Architect

Rating 1 Point

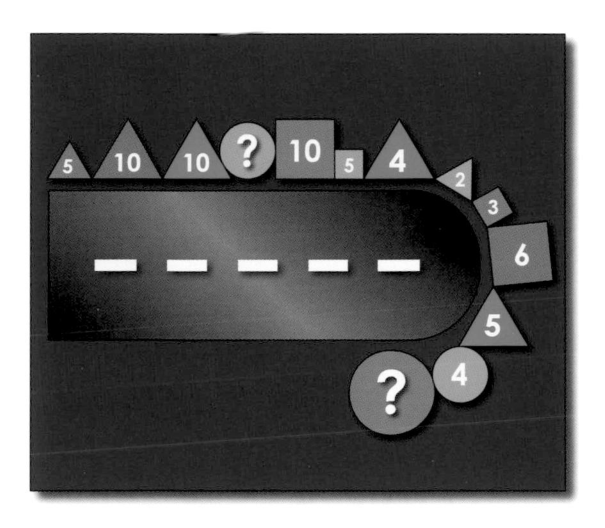

Mr Plann, the architect, is designing a very unusual street – his initial drawings are shown. The houses are all different shapes, and there seems to be no pattern to the house numbers. However, there is a logic behind his designs – can you identify the sequence and work out what the missing house numbers are?

Awful Architect - Solution

The numbers are 8 and 9. The ruling is that if the same shape and size of shape appears next in line, the number remains the same. If the same shape appears but twice the size, the number doubles. If the same shape appears, but half the size, the number is halved. If the next shape in line has less sides than the previous shape, the number decreases by 1. If the next shape in line has more sides it increases by 1.

Magic Square

Rating 1 Point

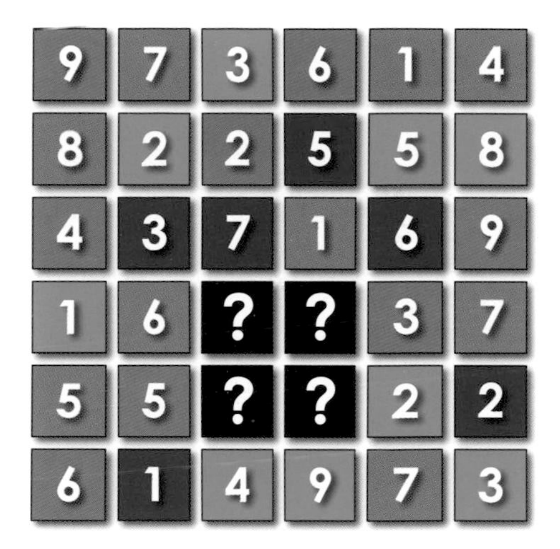

'Is this a magic number square?' asked Susan. *'No, it's not'* replied Tony, *'but it is an exercise in logic as there is a pattern to the way the numbers appear'*. *'I get it'* said Susan triumphantly, *'and I can now work out what numbers should replace the question marks!'* Can you?

Magic Square - Solution

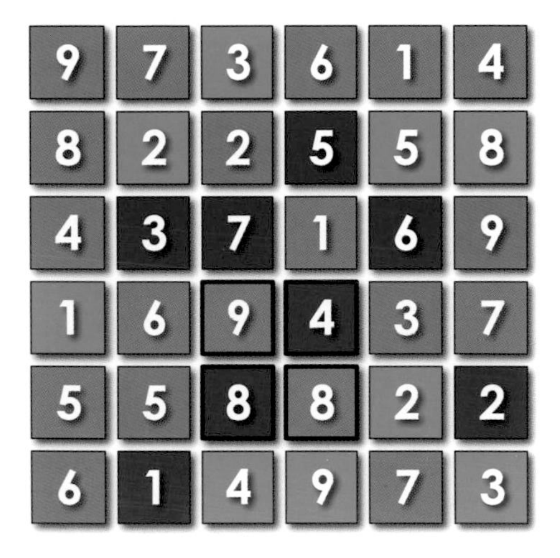

Start at the bottom right-hand corner and work up the end column and then back down the next column, repeating the sequence 327984156.

Big Cat Bother

Rating 2 Points

Which circus lion is the odd one out?

Big Cat Bother - Solution

GUY.
His number should be 53. The number represents the sum of the positions in the alphabet of each letter in his name – e.g. Ben = 2 + 5 + 14.

Daylight Robbery

Rating 2 Points

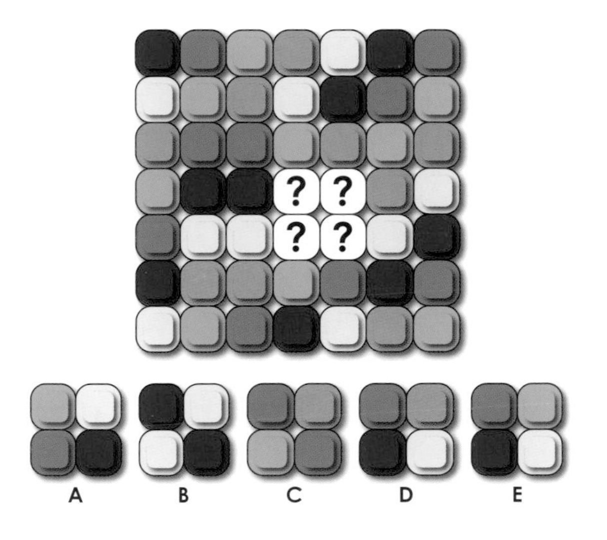

The cat-burglar has almost gained access to the vault. She has managed to key all but four of the correct colors into the code entry pad. Can you see which colors should replace the question marks?

Daylight Robbery - Solution

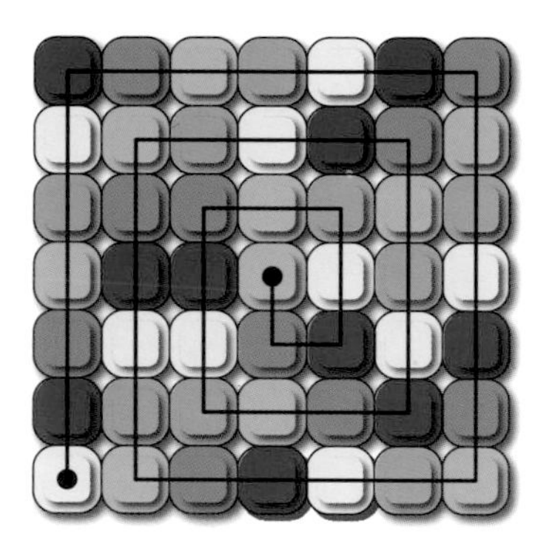

A.
Start at the bottom left-hand corner and work up the first column then round the perimeter clockwise and spiralling into the centre, repeating the sequence: yellow/red/blue/green/pink.

Shape Shift

Rating 3 Points

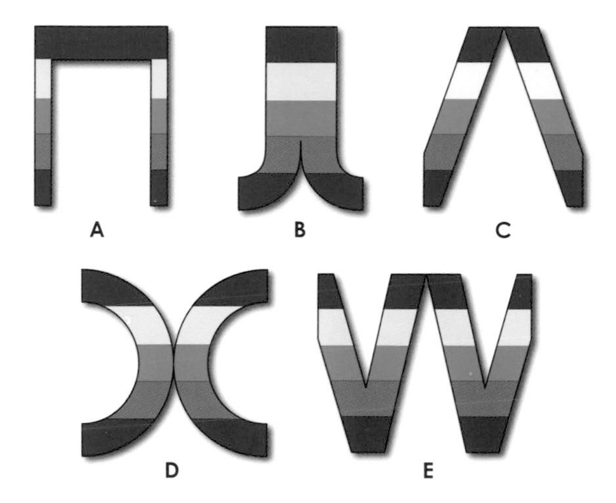

Archie the architect has designed some ornamental constructions for the front lawn of a school. However, he's noticed that one of the shapes is out of sequence – can you see which one it is?

Shape Shift - Solution

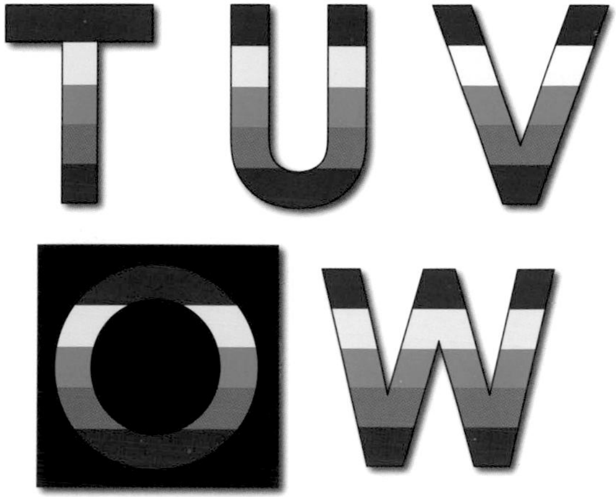

D.
They are the letters T U V O W, cut in half and reversed, with O being out of sequence.

Geography Guess

Rating 1 Point

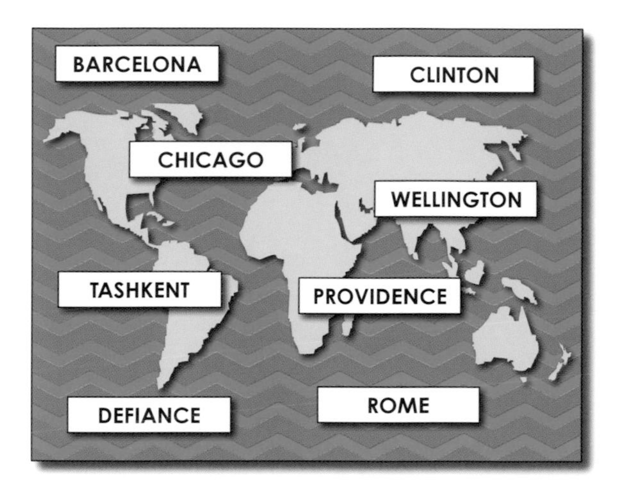

Mrs Megalopolis is a geography teacher. She has asked her class to spot which of the places shown is the odd one out. Can you work it out?

Geography Guess - Solution

Wellington. It is on latitude 41°S.
All the others are on latitude 41°N.

Thirsty Work

Rating 2 Points

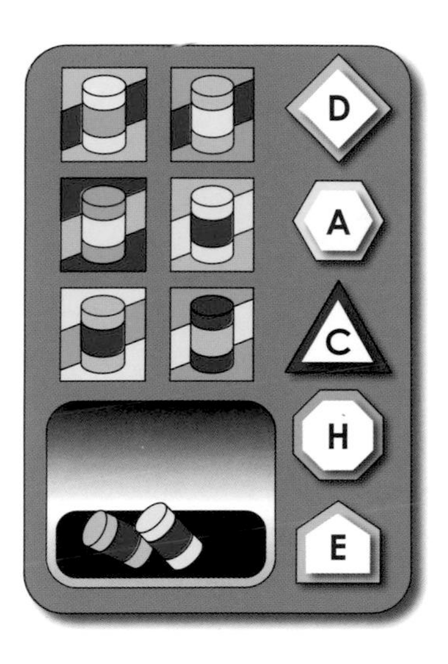

Which drinks machine button
does not fit the sequence?

Thirsty Work - Solution

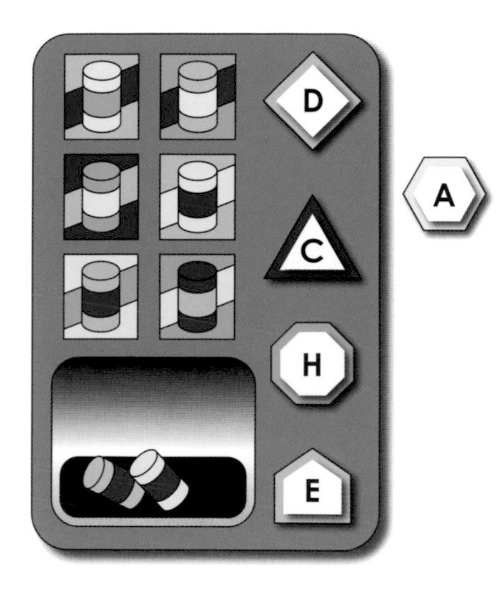

A.

The place of the letter in the alphabet corresponds to the number of sides of the button shape.
For example: D is the 4th letter and its shape has 4 sides.

Table Arrangement

Rating 3 Points

A B C D

Jane is making herself a coffee table decorated with individual tiles. The overall design incorporates a logical sequence. Which tile completes the design?

Table Arrangement - Solution

D.

In each row, the inner shape becomes the outer shape of the next tile pattern. In each row the background and third layer color change places, tile by tile and colors move up a layer in the next row.

DIY Disaster

Rating 2 Points

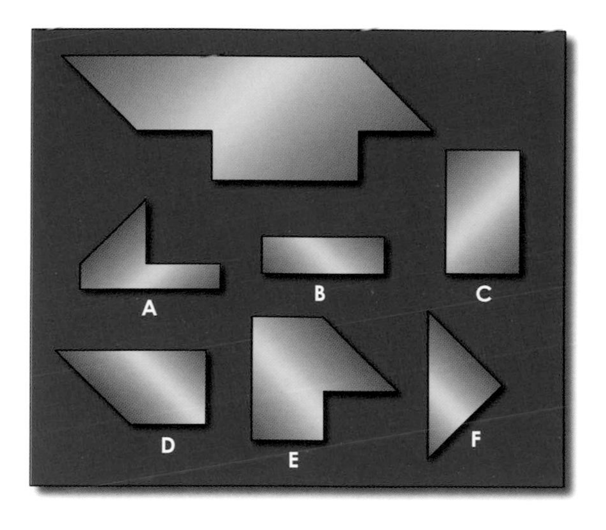

Fred bought a flat-pack shelving unit. It took him ages to figure out how to put it together. There were too many pieces. Which of the pieces in the sequence are not needed?

DIY Disaster – Solution

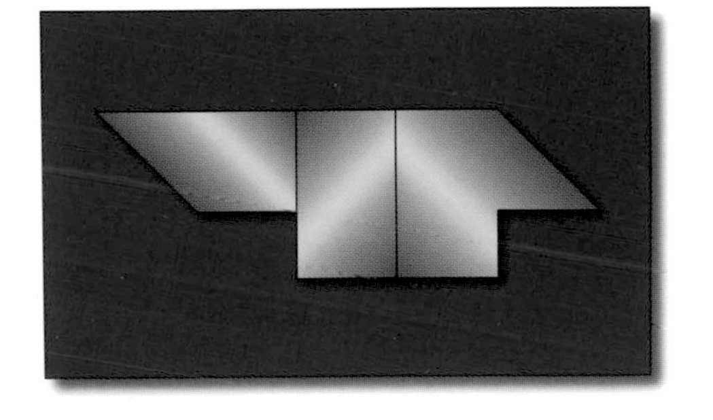

A, B, F are not needed.

Round the World

Rating 1 Point

What's the missing stop on the round-the-world tour?

Round the World - Solution

Florence.
Initial letters of towns/cities are O, T, T, F, F, S, S, E, N – the same as One, Two, Three, Four, Five, Six, Seven, Eight, Nine.

Strange Sequence

Rating 1 Point

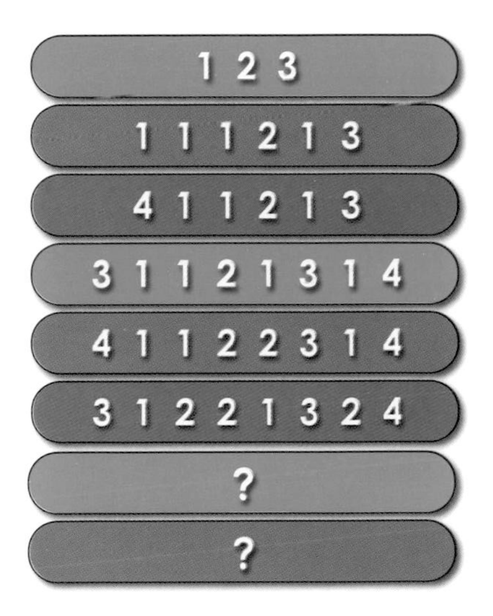

"Look at this sequence" said Peter, *"see if you can puzzle it out, and then tell me what the next two numbers should be"*. Alice thought very hard before realizing that something very strange was about to happen with the sequence. Can you work it out?

Strange Sequence - Solution

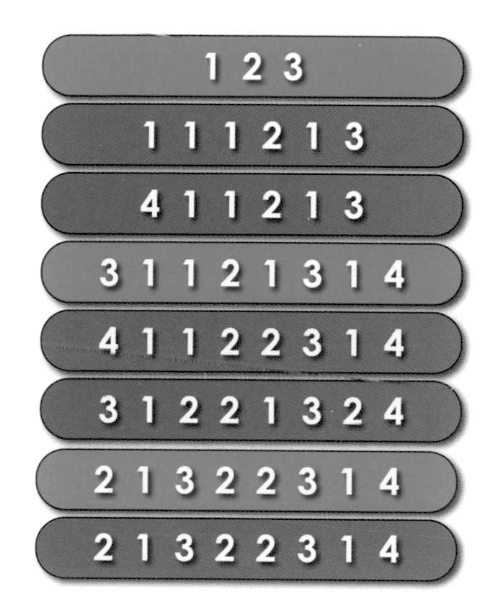

Each number describes the number above, starting with the smallest digits first. So 123 is followed by 1 x 1, 1 x 2, 1 x 3 (111213)
After 31221324 the sequence recurs with the number 21322314 (2 x 1, 3 x 2, 2 x 3, 1 x 4).

Math Muddle

Rating 2 Points

Jenny and Tom were in their Math lesson at school.
"What is the next number in this sequence?" asked Jenny.
"Seems an easy one" replied Tom. *"Now let me see, there is a difference of 55 between the first two numbers, then 15, then 15 again, therefore, I suppose it must be either a difference of 55 again, or a difference of 15, but logically there is no way of telling".*
"Yes there is" said Jenny, *"think again very carefully."*
Can you work it out?

Math Muddle - Solution

The numbers are in fact clock times, but without the dot in between hours and minutes, with 15 minutes added each time, i.e. 3.55, 4.10, 4.25, 4.40, 4.55.

Sweet Success

Rating 3 Points

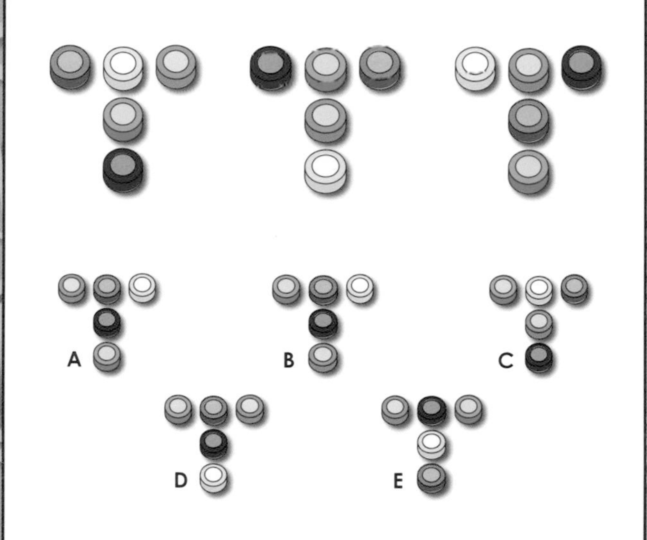

"If you can guess what comes next in the sequence, I'll give you all of the sweets" says Anna to Jack. Jack scratches his head and thinks carefully. At last he says, *"Ah, I think I've got it..."*. Can you work it out too?

Sweet Success - Solution

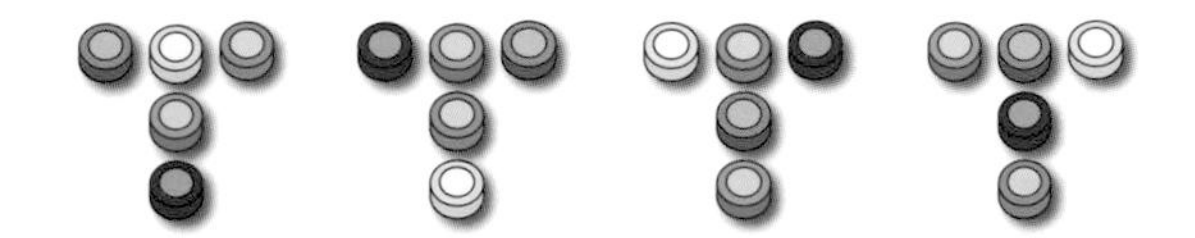

From stage to stage the colors move as follows:

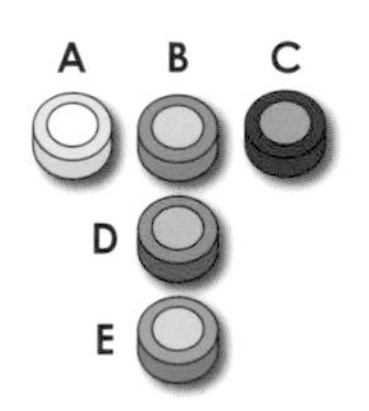

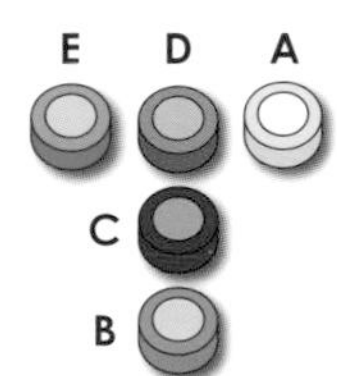

B.

Gridlock

Rating 2 Points

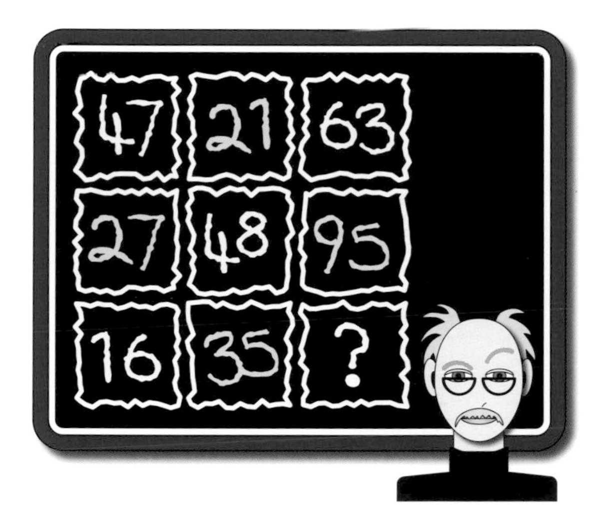

Professor Swott has drawn a grid on the blackboard. He's asked his class to tell him what number is missing from the bottom right-hand corner. Can you help them?

Gridlock - Solution

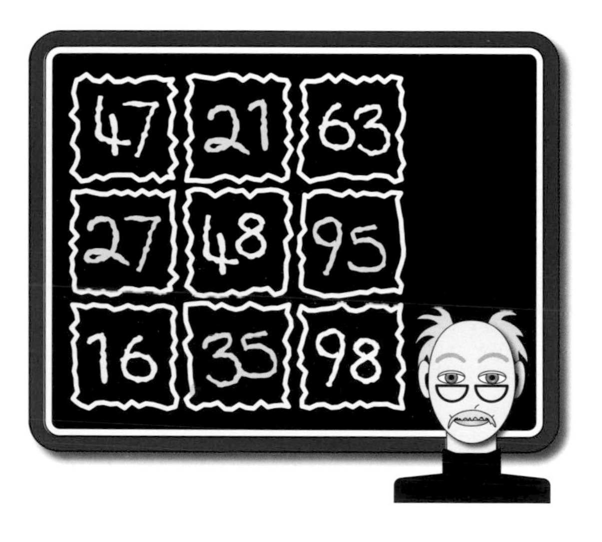

98.
Start at the top left-hand square and work along the top row, then back along the second and back along the third, repeating the numbers 472163598 in the same sequence.

Accessorize

Rating 1 Point

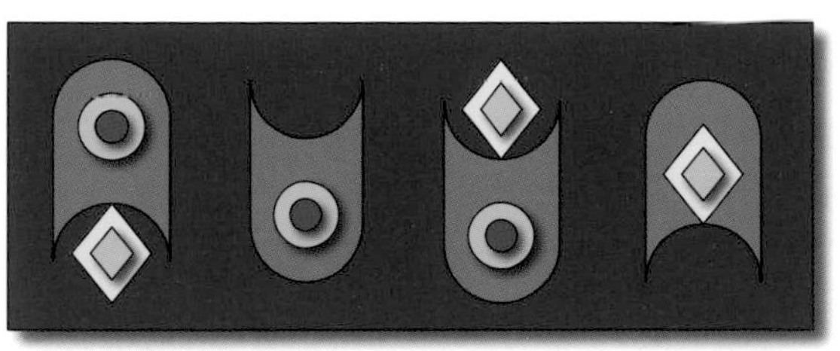

Monday Tuesday Wednesday Thursday

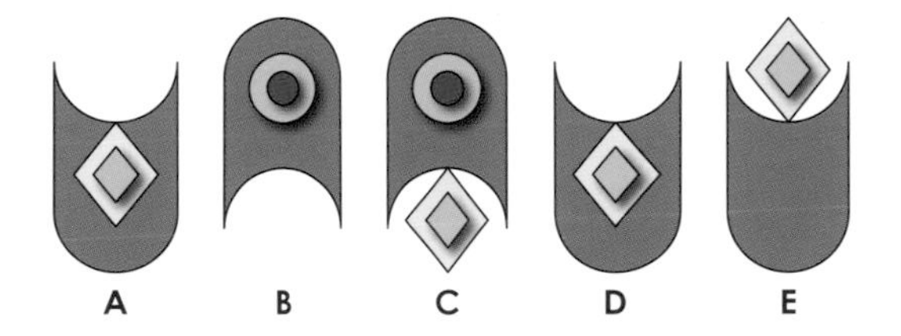

Caroline has a rather unusual brooch.
Each day she wears it in a slightly different way. Can you work out how it will look on Friday?

Accessorize - Solution

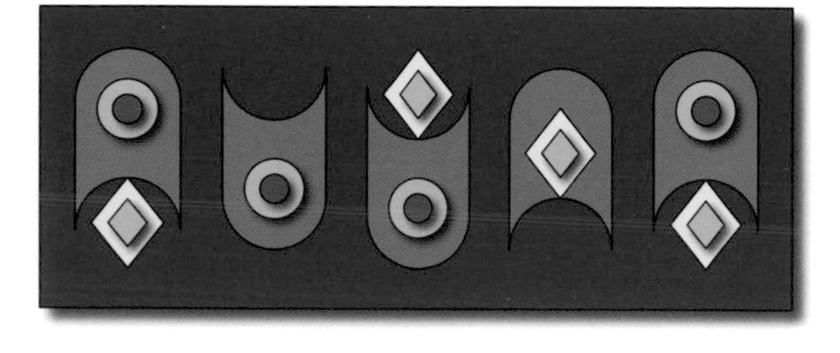

C.
First the large shape flips down, then the small shape flips up. Then the large shape flips up, then the small shape flips down. At stage 2 the small shape is hidden behind the large shape.

Spy School

Rating 2 Points

Boris the Russian spy wanted his British counterpart to follow his numerical code to the letter, so he decided to test him out by sending the sequence above. What was the next number in the sequence?

Spy School - Solution

The words 'one, two, three, four' etc, are converted into their numerical equivalent – e.g. ONE is 15 (for O), 14 (for N), 5 (for E). The next number in the sequence is 7, which when converted into its numerical equivalent gives the above answer.

Perplexing Pattern

Rating 3 Points

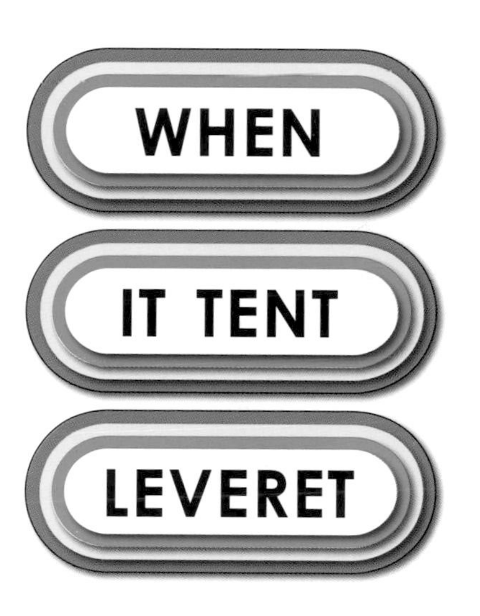

What is missing from this sequence?

Perplexing Pattern - Solution

Eleven.
The words are anagrams of the letters of:
TEN TWELVE THIRTEEN.

Howzat!

Rating 1 Point

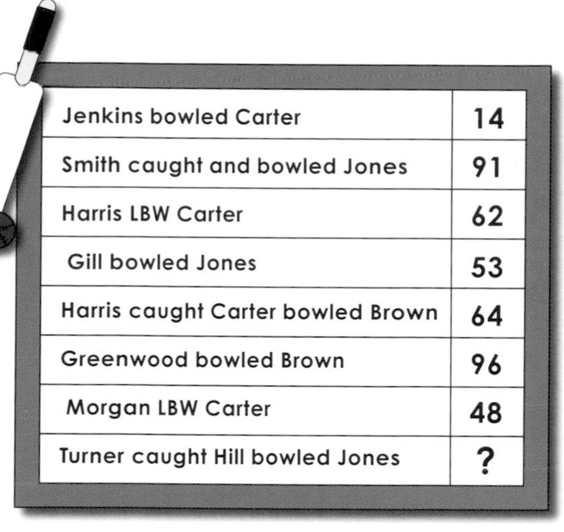

Jenkins bowled Carter	14
Smith caught and bowled Jones	91
Harris LBW Carter	62
Gill bowled Jones	53
Harris caught Carter bowled Brown	64
Greenwood bowled Brown	96
Morgan LBW Carter	48
Turner caught Hill bowled Jones	?

The chart shows the batting performance of the cricket team so far. How many did Turner score, if he reached double figures?

Howzat! - Solution

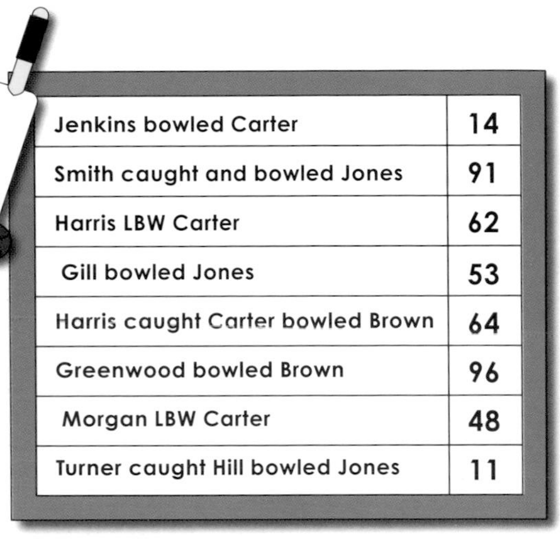

Jenkins bowled Carter	14
Smith caught and bowled Jones	91
Harris LBW Carter	62
Gill bowled Jones	53
Harris caught Carter bowled Brown	64
Greenwood bowled Brown	96
Morgan LBW Carter	48
Turner caught Hill bowled Jones	11

11.

The sequence follows a series of square numbers split into groups of 2 i.e. 1, 4, 9, 16, 25, 36, 49, 64, 81, 100.

To score points in this chapter, you need to provide the correct solution to each puzzle within ten minutes.

To see individual ratings for each puzzle – look under the title of each question. Once you have completed the chapter, turn to page 146, for help adding up your score.

Then turn to page 191 to see how you fared overall in the Brain-Boosting Sequence Puzzle Challenge.

Chapter 4 - Scoring

Puzzle points for correct answer

Flower Power	**2**	Fruity Fiasco	**1**
Cure for Hiccups	**1**	Speedy Sprinters	**2**
Knights of Laguna	**1**	General Knowledge	**3**
Fido's Feat	**2**	Totally Tricky	**2**
Dolphin Dilemma	**3**	Colorful Chart	**3**
Good Deal	**1**	Party People	**1**
Road Trip	**2**	Hieroglypics	**2**
Alien Code	**1**	Piece of a Picture	**3**
Moon Message	**3**	Hexagon	**2**
Cheerleaders	**2**	Letter Sequence	**1**
Chimp Challenge	**1**	Stage Fright	**1**

YOUR TOTAL

/40

Flower Power

Rating 2 Points

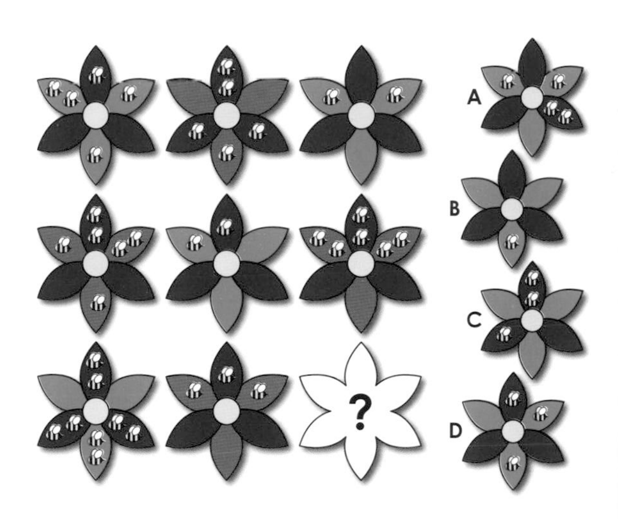

Professor Cosine is a mathematician, and keen botanist. He's studying a rare flowering bush, which is very popular with bees. While he's studying the bush, he notices a sequence emerging. Which flower would complete the sequence?

Flower Power - Solution

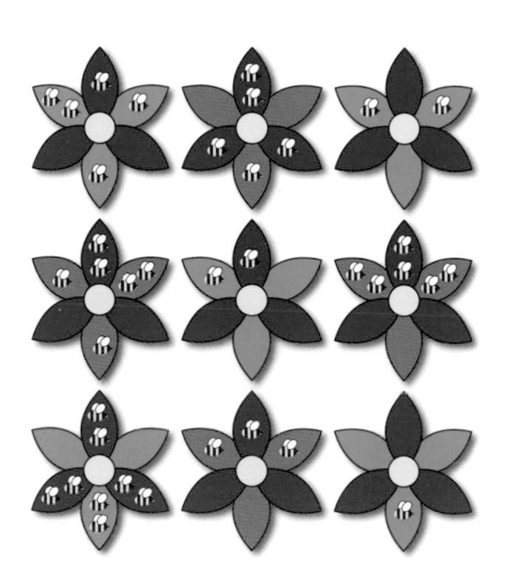

B.

Each row represents a sum. The dots on the top petals on each flower are plus amounts, those below minus amounts. The last flower in each row gives the answer.

Sums are:

Top row (4 – 1 = 3) + (2 – 3 = -1) = 2

Middle row (5 – 1 = 4) + (2 – 0 = 2) = 6

Bottom row (2 – 6 = -4) + (3 – 0 = 3) = -1

Cure for Hiccups

Rating 1 Point

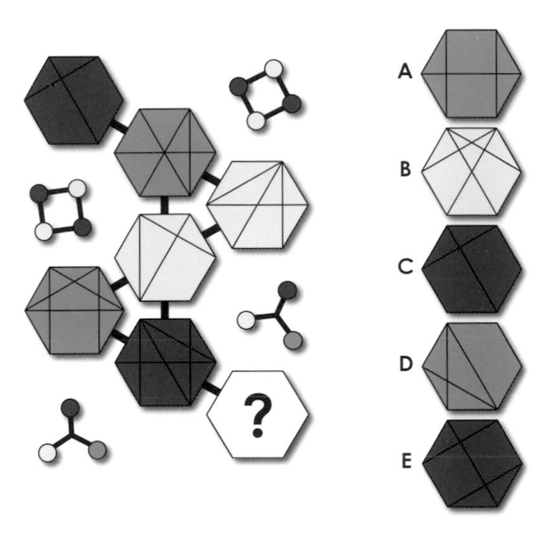

Professor Vector is creating a cure for hiccups.
He has successfully assembled six compounds, which will form the basis of his cure, but needs to add an additional compound in order to make the cure 100% effective.
Can you work out which is the final compound?

Cure for Hiccups - Solution

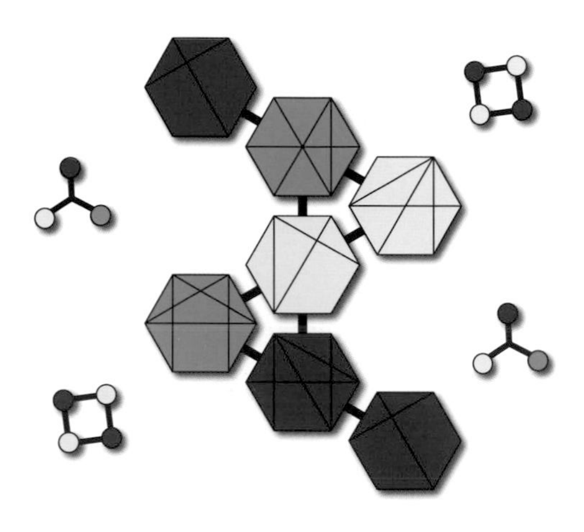

Compound C.
From top to bottom the contents of the third hexagon in each connected row of three is determined by the contents of the first two hexagons in the row. Lines that appear in the first two hexagons are carried forward to the third hexagon, except when two lines appear in the same position, in which case they are cancelled out.

Knights of Laguna

Rating 1 Point

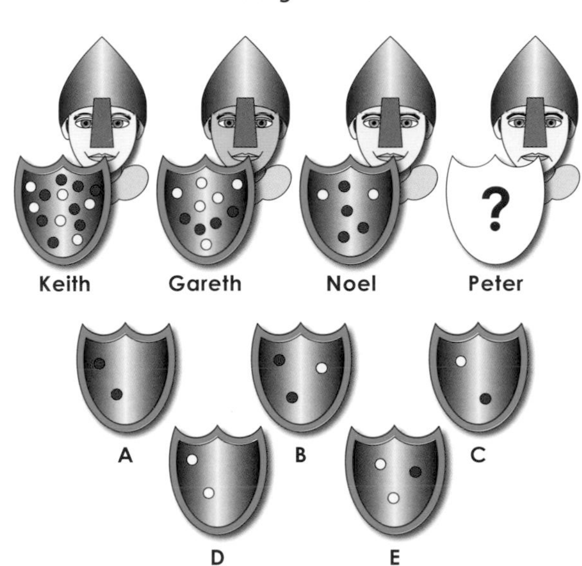

The 4 brave Knights of Laguna have shields that look similar, but that differ slightly from each other. From the sequence that they follow, can you work out which shield should be given to Peter?

Knights of Laguna - Solution

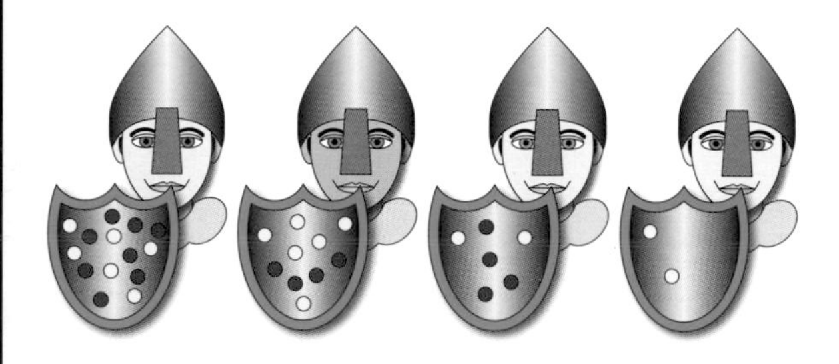

D.

The second shield has two less red dots than there are yellow dots in the first shield and two less yellow dots than there are red dots. The sequence continues in this way so that in the answer there are 4 – 2 = 2 yellow dots and 2 – 2 = 0 red dots.

Fido's Feat

Rating 2 Points

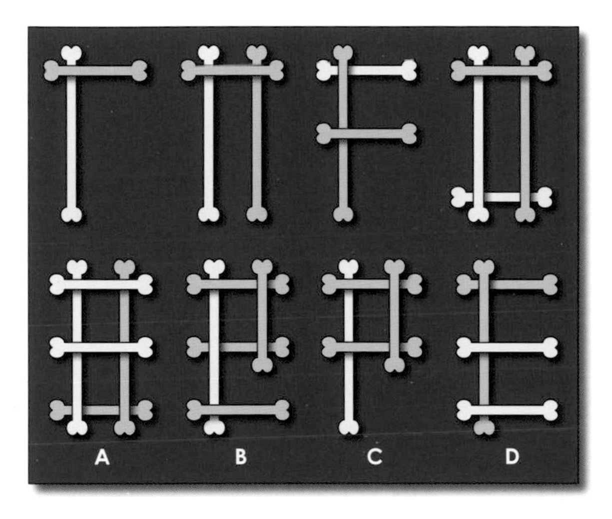

Fido the Amazing Performing Dog has arranged his bones in the pattern shown above. Can you guess what comes next?

Fido's Feat - Solution

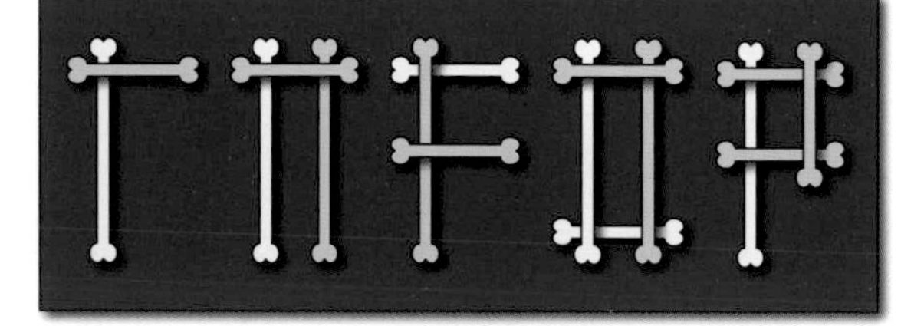

C.
The number of right-angles in each of the figures increases by one each time.

Dolphin Dilemma

Rating 3 Points

Donald the Dolphin is performing one of his favorite tricks. His trainer hangs cards above his pool. Donald then has to work out the sequence and squeak the number that should replace the question mark. Can you beat him to it?

Dolphin Dilemma - Solution

6.

Donald works round the ring of figures in a clockwise direction. The hexagon/diamond is 5 less than the previous figure, the circle/triangle is plus 3, the square/circle plus 4, and the pentagon/circle is minus 2.

Good Deal

Rating 1 Point

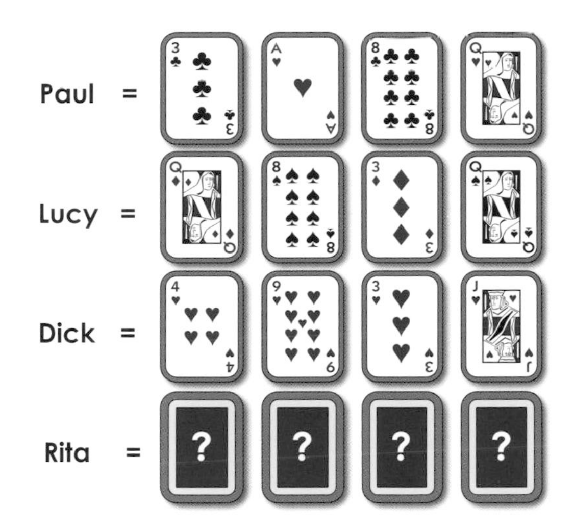

Paul and Lucy invite Dick and Rita for a game of cards. Paul, Lucy and Dick are dealt the following cards – what does Rita get?

Good Deal - Solution

Rita = 5♠ 9♦ 7♠ A♦

5 of spades, 9 of diamonds, 7 of spades, ace of diamonds.
Hearts and clubs represent the boys' names:
A = Ace of hearts
B = 2 of hearts
C = 3 of hearts
D 4 E 5 F 6 G 7 H 8 I 9 J 10 K Jack L Queen M King
N = Ace of clubs
O = 2 of clubs etc
Diamonds and spades represent the girls' names:
A = Ace of diamonds
B = 2 of diamonds
C 3 of diamonds D 4 E 5 F 6 G 7 H 8 I 9 J 10 K Jack L Queen
M = King
N = Ace of spades
O = 2 of spades etc

Road Trip

Rating 2 Points

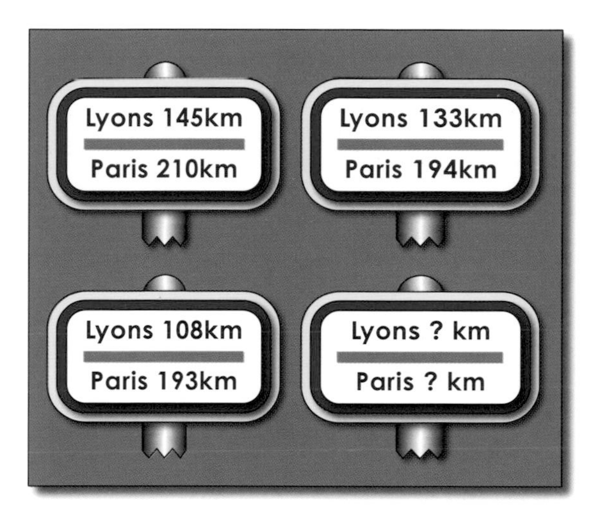

While driving through central France, Pierre sees the first sign. A little while later he sees the second sign. Later still he sees the third sign. Can you work out what the next sign will say, and can you also calculate how far from Paris Pierre will be when he gets as near as he is going to get to Lyons?

Road Trip - Solution

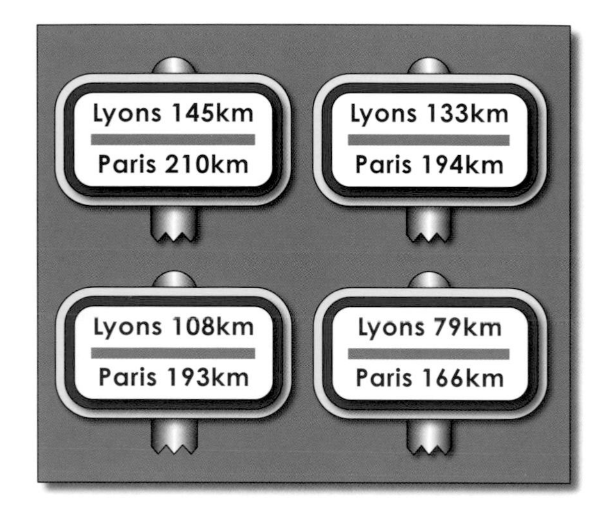

The number of kilometres travelled is determined by the numerical equivalent of the letters of the cities. Lyons is approached in sections of 12, 25, 15, 14 and 19km (L = 12, Y = 25, O = 15 etc). Paris is approached in sections of 16, 1, 18, 9 and 19km (P = 16, A = 1 etc). When the letters of the city names run out, Pierre will be 147 km away from Paris.

Alien Code

Rating 1 Point

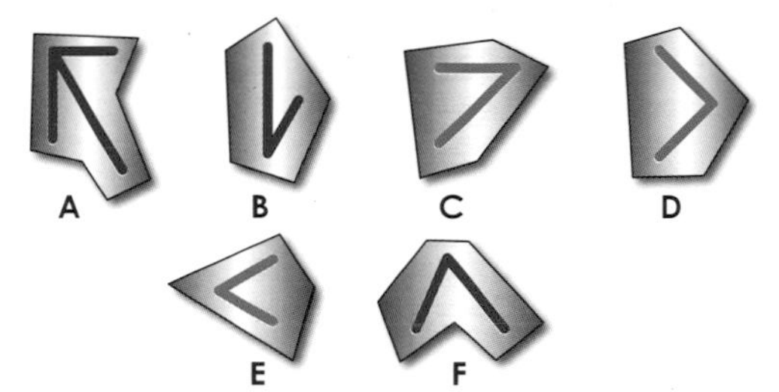

Captain Meteor has boarded the Alien spaceship. He's face to face with what looks like a large door, with symbols etched into the metal. It appears that he has to push the correct button in order to open the door. Can you help him to reveal the sequence and push the correct button?

Alien Code - Solution

B.

The fourth figure added to the first produces:

The fifth figure added to the second produces:

Therefore, the sixth figure added to the third should produce:

Moon Message

Rating 3 Points

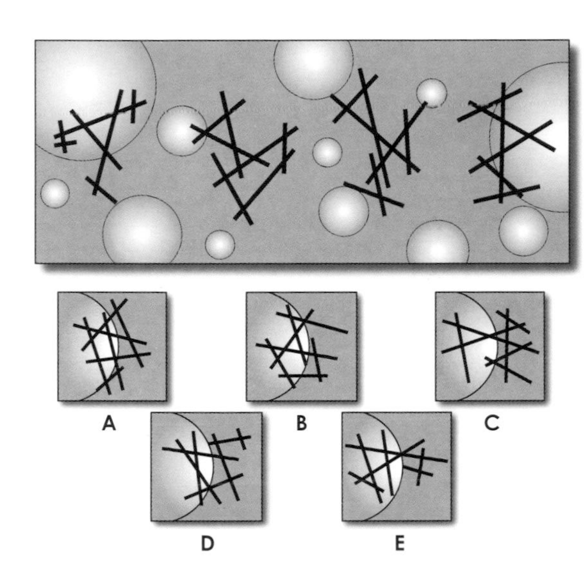

Two astronauts have landed on the moon. Their spacecraft has dislodged some moon dust to reveal the following symbols. While Bob puzzles over their meaning, Elizabeth brushes away some more dust to reveal a fifth symbol. Can you work out which symbol she reveals?

Moon Message - Solution

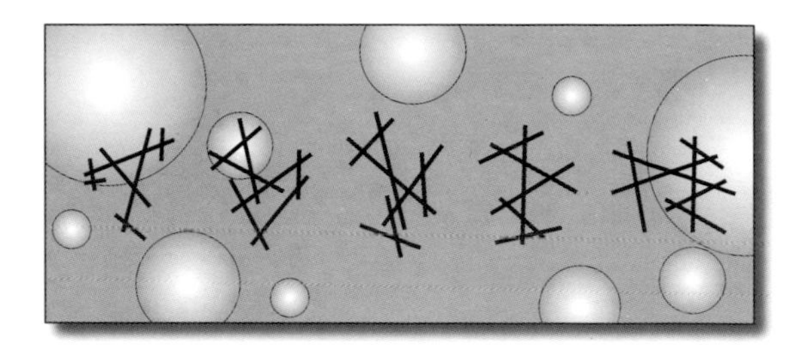

C.

The lines are arranged so that first they form one triangle, then two triangles, then three triangles, then four triangles, and finally five triangles.

Cheerleaders

Rating 2 Points

The Funbury Cheerleaders are demonstrating their grand finale formation. The numbers on their shirts seem at first glance to have been inserted completely at random, however, there is a pattern to them. Can you solve the puzzle and say what number should appear on the shirt of the cheerleader in the bottom right-hand corner?

Cheerleaders - Solution

9.

Looking down each row from north-east to south-west, starting with 7 at the top, each row is the reverse of the previous row with the smallest digit discarded, i.e. 748293, 39847, 7489, 987, 79, 9.

Chimp Challenge

Rating 1 Point

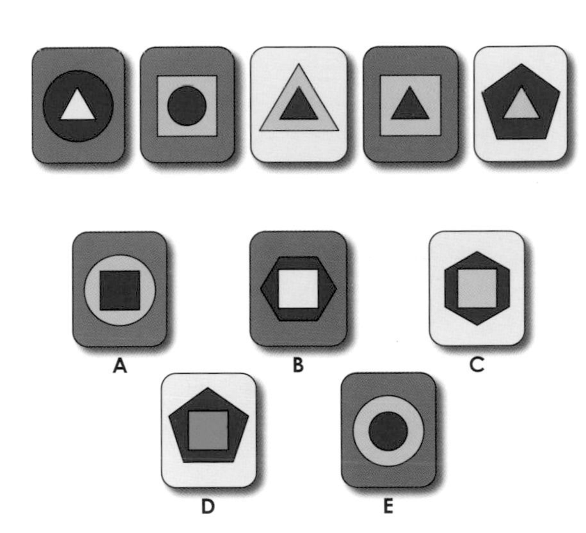

Doris, the highly intelligent chimp is shown this sequence of flash cards. She's already worked out what card should come next – can you?

Chimp Challenge - Solution

D.
The total number of sides in each pair of figures increases by 1 each time, i.e. circle + triangle = 4 sides, circle + square = 5 sides etc.

Fruity Fiasco

Rating 1 Point

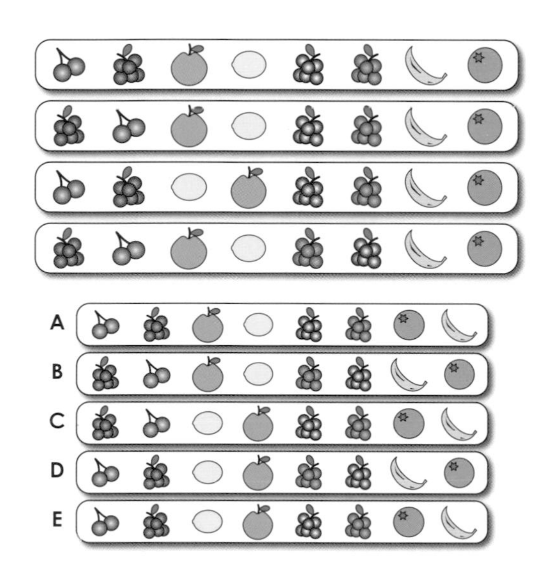

Simon is playing on the biggest fruit machine in the world. He has had four turns, with the results shown. He's spotted a pattern emerging and has worked out what the next sequence should be. What comes next?

Fruity Fiasco - Solution

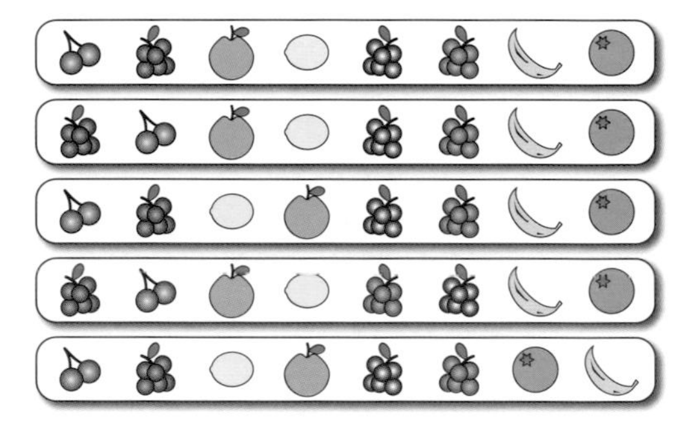

E.

At each stage a pair of fruits swaps round, working from left to right. After they have swapped round they continue to swap round at each stage.

Speedy Sprinters

Rating 2 Points

The photo finish shows the positions of the runners at the end of the race. Unfortunately the numbers on the two runners finishing 6th and 7th are blurred. However, from the photo finish, a sequence can been seen – from this sequence, can you work out what the numbers of the last two runners should be?

Speedy Sprinters - Solution

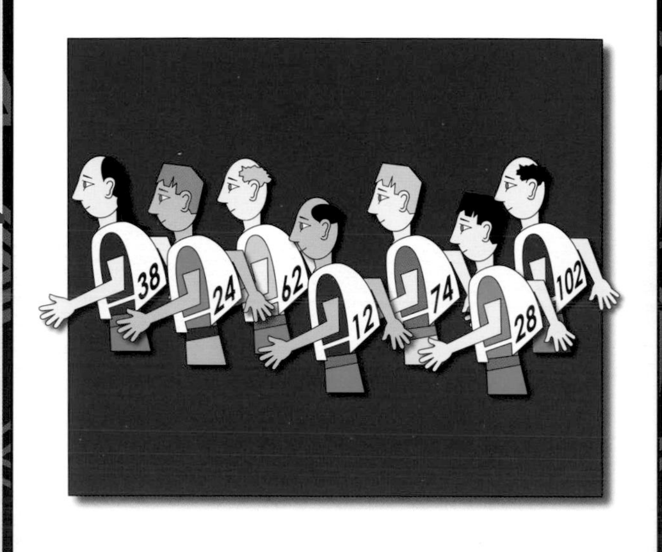

3 x 8 = 24, 38 + 24 = 62, 6 x 2 = 12,
62 + 12 = 74, 7 x 4 = 28, 74 + 28
= 102.

General Knowledge

Rating 3 Points

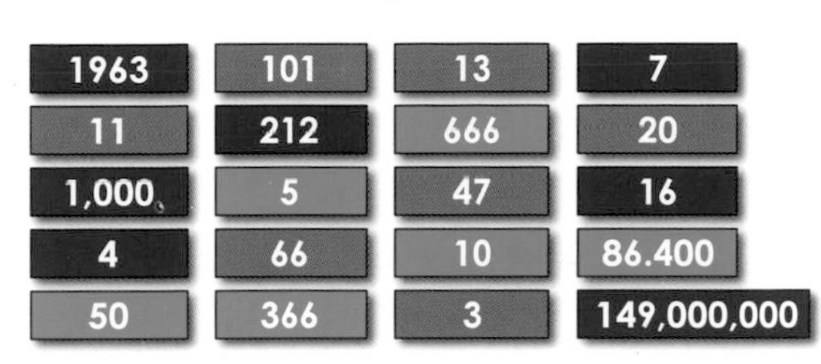

1963	101	13	7
11	212	666	20
1,000	5	47	16
4	66	10	86.400
50	366	3	149,000,000

1. Year of First Woman in Space
2. Distance of Earth from Sun in km
3. Cubic centimetres in a litre
4. Witches in Macbeth
5. Numbers on a dart board
6. Mark of the beast
7. Seconds in a day
8. Dalmatians
9. Skittles in a bowling alley
10. Minutes of sound on a CD
11. Days in a leap year
12. Atomic Number of silver
13. Fahrenheit boiling point of water
14. Storm force on the Beaufort wind scale
15. States in the USA
16. Elements
17. Players in a Rugby Team
18. Books in the Bible
19. Ages of Man
20. Pawns on a chess board
21. Great Lakes

One of the list above is not included in the sequence shown. Which one?

General Knowledge - Solution

1. Year of First Woman in Space = 1963
2. Distance of Earth from Sun in km = 149,000,000
3. Cubic centimetres in a litre = 1,000
4. Witches in Macbeth = 3
5. Numbers on a dart board = 20
6. Mark of the beast = 666
7. Seconds in a day = 86,400
8. Dalmatians = 101
9. Skittles in a bowling alley = 10
10. Minutes of sound on a CD
11. Days in a leap year = 366
12. Atomic Number of silver = 47
13. Fahrenheit boiling point of water = 212
14. Storm force on the Beaufort wind scale = 11
15. States in the USA = 50
16. Elements = 4
17. Players in a Rugby Team = 13
18. Books in the Bible = 66
19. Ages of Man = 7
20. Pawns on a chess board = 16
21. Great Lakes = 5

Minutes of sound on a CD (74).

Totally Tricky

Rating 2 Points

9, 13, 14, 21, 38, 40, 50, 52

20, 22, 35, 39, 55, ?

Figure out what the first sequence represents, then complete the second sequence...

Totally Tricky - Solution

20, 22, 35, 39, 55, 61

61.
The first sequence is the position of all the letter Ts in the question. The second sequence is the position of each letter S.

Colorful Chart

Rating 3 Points

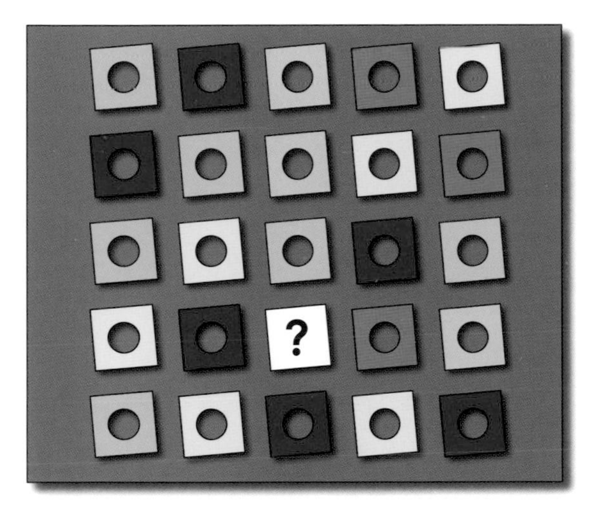

Each color in the grid represents a number, always the same number. The numbers in each horizontal and vertical row add up to 30. Can you work out which number fits in the blank square?

Colorful Chart - Solution

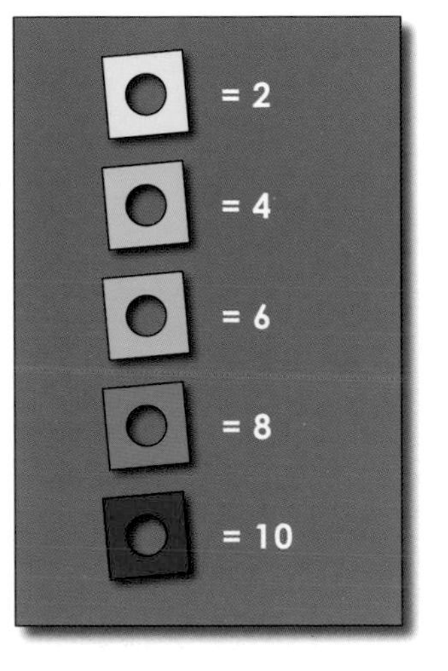

 fits in the blank square.

Party People

Rating 1 Point

The guests to Jenny's birthday party turned up in the order shown above. Of the four remaining guests to arrive, Samuel, Valery, James and Fergal, who arrived next?

Party People - Solution

James

James.
The vowels in each name are in pairs, AE, EI, IO, OU, UA, therefore the next name will be AE. The first letter of each name is in the first half of the alphabet, the last letter is in the second half. Therefore, James has J in 1st half and S in 2nd half. James is the only name that fits these conditions.

Hieroglyphics

Rating 2 Points

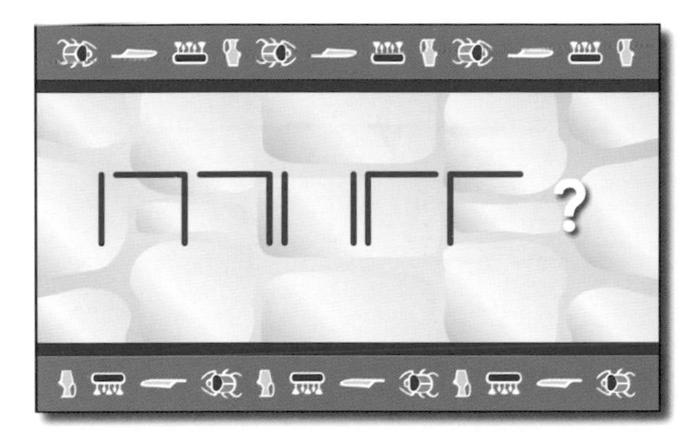

Two explorers entered the ancient Egyptian pyramid and saw strange markings carved into a wall. *"Aha, ancient hieroglyphics"* said one of the explorers. *"I don't think so"* said the other, *"in fact I believe these markings are quite modern, in fact there appears to be a sequence – I think I can easily draw the next in the series with my piece of chalk."*

Hieroglyphics - Solution

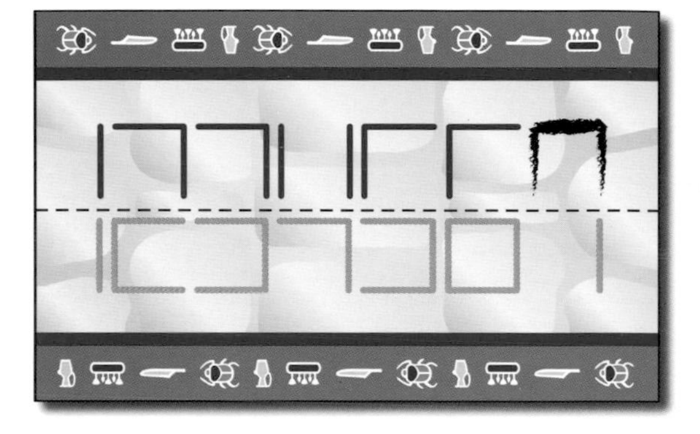

They are digital figures with the top half missing.

Piece of a Picture

Rating 3 Points

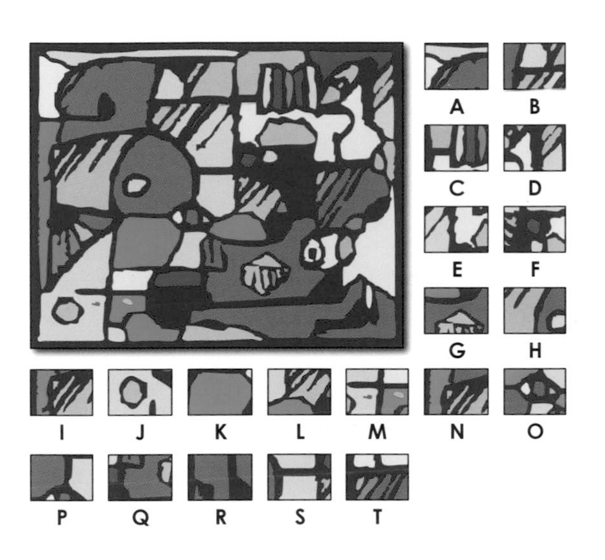

Which of the pieces above is not part of the main picture?

Piece of a Picture - Solution

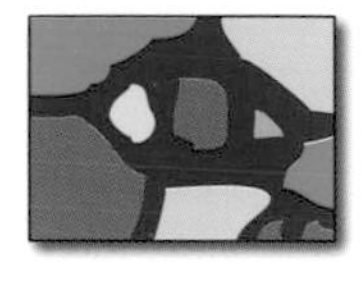

O.

Hexagon

Rating 2 Points

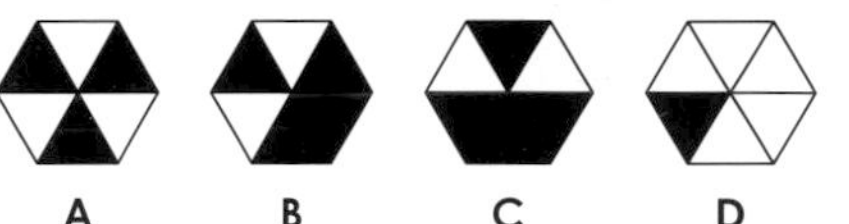

Which hexagon should replace the question mark?

Hexagon - Solution

B.

The contents of each hexagon are determined by the contents of the two hexagons immediately below it. When two identical segments appear black in these two hexagons, they appear as white segments in the hexagon above, and vice versa. When identically positioned segments appear black/white in these two hexagons, they appear as white in the hexagon above.

Letter Sequence

Rating 1 Point

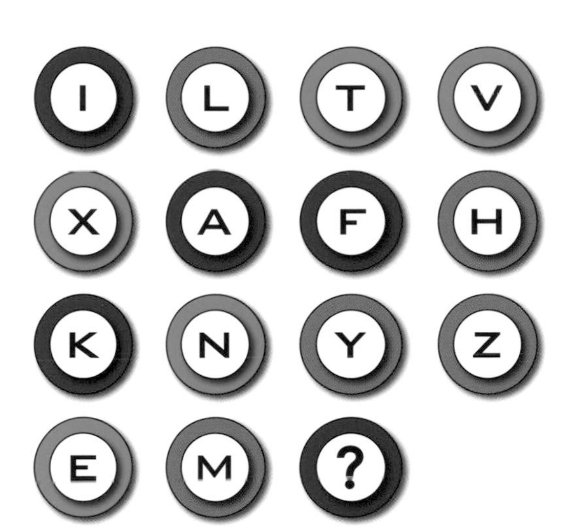

What is the next letter in this sequence?

Letter Sequence - Solution

W.
The sequence features all the letters of the alphabet that are made up of straight lines, in alphabetical order, first those with one stroke, then those with two strokes, three strokes etc.

Stage Fright

Rating 1 Point

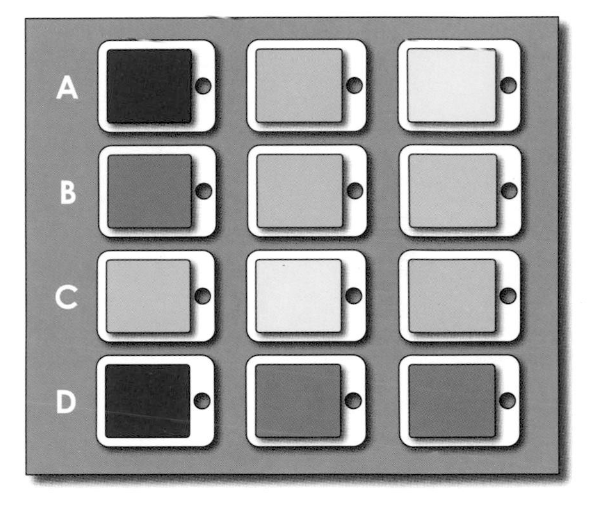

Roger is working behind the scenes on the forthcoming production of 'Chicago'. He refers to a color chart, but notices an error in the chart – one of the rows of color sequences is incorrect. Can you see which it is and why?

Stage Fright - Solution

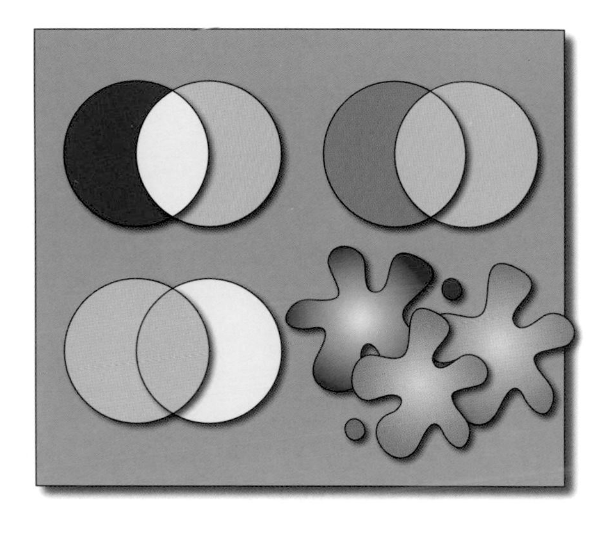

C.

Roger is the lighting technician for the production. He notices that the color in the last box in each sequence of three is the result of mixing light of the first two colors. In row C it is the result of mixing paint pigment of the first two colors.

Overall Scoring Page

Chapter	Score Card	Potential Score	Your Score
1	Page 8	40	
2	Page 54	40	
3	Page 100	40	
4	Page 146	40	
		GRAND TOTAL	

Anyone who has scored more than 120 points can afford to sit back and feel smug. Well done, you're in the top 25%!

Anyone who got between 80 and 120 points should be content knowing they got more than half of the puzzles correct.

Those with less than 80 points however, should turn over to page 192 for more information on Lagoon's other Brain-Boosting titles – you really should do a bit more practice!

OTHER BRAIN-BOOSTING TITLES AVAILABLE FROM LAGOON BOOKS

BRAIN-BOOSTING CRYPTOLOGY PUZZLES
(ISBN: 1902813545)

BRAIN-BOOSTING QUANTUM PUZZLES
(ISBN: 1902813529)

BRAIN BOOSTING VISUAL LOGIC PUZZLES
(ISBN: 1902813200)

BRAIN BOOSTING LATERAL THINKING PUZZLES
(ISBN: 1902813227)

BRAIN-BOOSTING CRYPTIC PUZZLES
(ISBN: 1902813219)

You can view our full range of puzzle books along with the full collection of Lagoon Books on our website:

www.lagoongames.com

LAGOON
BOOKS